THE ULTIMATE
HOUSTON ASTROS
TRIVIA BOOK

A Collection of Amazing Trivia Quizzes
and Fun Facts for Die-Hard Astros Fans!

Ray Walker

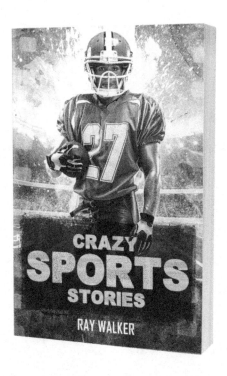

CONTENTS

INTRODUCTION

The Houston Astros were established in 1962. They started as the Houston Colt .45s, and have proven themselves to be a team who fights hard and is a force to be reckoned with in the MLB.

The Astros currently call Minute Maid Park home, which opened in 2000. They play in one of the most difficult divisions in baseball, the American League West, alongside the Oakland Athletics, Los Angeles Angels of Anaheim, Seattle Mariners, and Texas Rangers. They currently hold one World Series championship, which they won in 2017. They were found to have stolen signs during that championship year, which has tainted their title in many eyes. They have also won the National League pennant in 2005 and the American League pennant twice (2017 and 2019). They are very often a threat in the American League West, having won the division three straight years from 2017-19, despite only being in the division since 2013. They also made the playoffs three times as the wild card in franchise history.

The thing about baseball is that it is a lot like life. There are good times and bad times, good days and bad days, but you have to do your absolute best to never give up. The Houston

Astros have proven that they refuse to give up and that they will do anything they need to do in order to bring a championship to the state of Texas. Winning is more than possible when you have a storied past like the Astros do. They have so much captivating history and so many undeniable player legacies to be profoundly proud of. Those legacies have been explored here, with stats in this book being updated as of the end of the 2020 season.

With such a storied team past that goes back generations, you're probably already very knowledgeable as the die-hard 'Stros fan that you are. Let's test that knowledge to see if you truly are the world's biggest Astros fan.

CHAPTER 1:

ORIGINS & HISTORY

QUIZ TIME!

1. Which of the following team names did the Astros franchise once go by?

   a. Cowboys

   b. Texans

   c. Colt .45s

   d. They have always been the Astros.

2. In what year was the Houston Astros franchise established?

   a. 1901

   b. 1955

   c. 1962

   d. 1969

3. The Astros' current home stadium is Minute Maid Park.

   a. True

   b. False

4. Which division do the Houston Astros play in currently?

   a. American League Central

   b. American League West

   c. National League West

   d. National League Central

5. The Houston Astros have NEVER won a wild card berth.

   a. True

   b. False

6. How many American League pennants has the Astros franchise won?

   a. 2

   b. 5

   c. 9

   d. 12

7. What is the name of the Astros' mascot?

   a. Pluto

   b. Starry

   c. Astros Aardvark

   d. Orbit

8. Who is the winningest manager in Houston Astros history?

   a. A.J. Hinch

   b. Art Howe

   c. Bill Virdon

   d. Terry Collins

9. What is the name of the Houston Astros' Triple A-Team, and where are they located?

   a. Louisville Bats
   b. Round Rock Express
   c. Rochester Red Wings
   d. Buffalo Bisons

10. Who was the first manager of the Astros franchise?

   a. Harry Craft
   b. Luman Harris
   c. Harry Walker
   d. Salty Parker

11. The Astros played in the NL West from 1969 to 1993, the NL Central from 1994 to 2012, before moving to the AL West in 2013.

   a. True
   b. False

12. What is the name of the Astros' current spring training home stadium?

   a. Publix Field
   b. Clover Park
   c. FitTeam Ballpark
   d. JetBlue Park

13. How many appearances has the Houston Astros franchise made in the MLB playoffs?

   a. 9
   b. 11

c. 14

d. 18

14. How many World Series titles have the Astros won?

    a. 1
    b. 2
    c. 3
    d. 4

15. The Astros won only one pennant during their time in the National League.

    a. True
    b. False

16. Which stadium was the first home stadium of the Houston Astros franchise?

    a. Houston Ballpark
    b. Astrodome
    c. Minute Maid Park
    d. Colt Stadium

17. How many NL West titles did the Houston Astros win between 1969-93?

    a. 2
    b. 4
    c. 7
    d. 9

18. How many NL Central titles did the Astros win between 1994-2012?

a. 2

b. 4

c. 6

d. 9

19. How many AL West titles have the Houston Astros won since 2013?

a. 0

b. 1

c. 2

d. 3

20. The Colt .45s changed their name to the Astros on December 1, 1964.

a. True

b. False

QUIZ ANSWERS

1. C – Colt .45s

2. C – 1962

3. A – True

4. B – American League West

5. B – False (They have won 3.)

6. A – 2

7. D – Orbit

8. C – Bill Virdon

9. B – Round Rock Express

10. A – Harry Craft

11. A – True

12. C – FitTeam Ballpark

13. C – 14

14. A – 1 (2017)

15. A – True (2005)

16. D – Colt Stadium

17. A – 2

18. B – 4

19. D – 3

20. A – True

DID YOU KNOW?

1. The Astros franchise has had 24 managers so far in their history. They include: Harry Craft, Luman Harris, Grady Hatton, Harry Walker, Salty Parker, Leo Durocher, Preston Gómez, Bill Virdon, Bob Lillis, Hall Lanier, Art Howe, Terry Collins, Larry Dierker, Matt Galante, Jimy Williams, Phil Garner, Cecil Cooper, Dave Clark, Brad Mills, Tony DeFrancesco, Bo Porter, Tom Lawless, A.J. Hinch, and Dusty Baker.

2. The Astros' current manager is Dusty Baker. He has previously managed the San Francisco Giants, Chicago Cubs, Cincinnati Reds, and the Washington Nationals.

3. Bill Virdon is the Houston Astros' all-time winningest manager with a record of 544-522 (.510).

4. Jim Umbricht was the first player to have his number retired by the Houston Astros. His number 32 was retired in 1965.

5. The Houston Astros have hosted three All-Star Games so far in franchise history. The first one took place in 1968 at the Astrodome, the second took place in 1986 at the Astrodome, and the third took place in 2004 at Minute Maid Park.

6. The Astros have had 13 no-hitters thrown in franchise history.

7. There has never been a perfect game thrown by an Astro in franchise history.

8. The Astros' Double-A team is the Corpus Christi Hooks.

9. Orbit is a lime green alien. Orbit was the Astros' mascot from 1990 to 1999, and then made a return in 2013 when the Astros moved to the AL West.

10. The Astrodome was the first domed sports stadium and was known as "the eighth wonder of the world." The Astros played there from 1965 to 1999.

CHAPTER 2:

JERSEYS & NUMBERS

QUIZ TIME!

1. In 1972, the Astros changed their uniform fabric to polyester. Belts were replaced by elastic waistbands, and jerseys were zipped up instead of buttoned.

    a. True

    b. False

2. The Astros' tequila sunrise uniforms debuted in _____.

    a. 1973

    b. 1974

    c. 1975

    d. 1976

3. From 2000 to 2012, the Astros ditched the color navy and used the colors brick red, sand, and black. When they moved to the AL West in 2013, they went back to an orange and navy color scheme.

    a. True

    b. False

4. Which of the following numbers is NOT retired by the Houston Astros?

    a. 5

    b. 7

    c. 12

    d. 34

5. What uniform number does second baseman Jose Altuve currently wear as a member of the Astros?

    a. 10

    b. 17

    c. 20

    d. 27

6. What uniform number did slugger Lance Berkman wear during his time with the Astros?

    a. 17

    b. 22

    c. 33

    d. Both A and B

7. Lance Berkman's uniform number is retired by the Houston Astros.

    a. True

    b. False

8. Only two Astros players have ever worn the uniform number 0 in franchise history. Those two players are Chase De Jong and who?

    a. John Mayberry

    b. Carlos Correa

c. L.J. Hoes

d. Mitch Williams

9. Which former Astros manager has his number 49 retired by the team?

   a. Larry Dierker

   b. Terry Collins

   c. Art Howe

   d. Harry Walker

10. The Astros had a shooting star on their jerseys from 1965 to 1970.

   a. True

   b. False

11. What are the Houston Astros' official team colors?

   a. Navy blue and orange

   b. Navy blue, orange, white

   c. Orange and white

   d. Navy blue, orange, white, black

12. Who was the first Astro to have his uniform number retired by the team?

   a. Don Wilson

   b. Nolan Ryan

   c. Jose Cruz

   d. Jim Umbricht

13. Craig Biggio is the latest to have his uniform number (7) retired by the Astros, on August 17, 2008.

a. True

b. False

14. What jersey number did Roger Clemens wear as an Astro?

    a. 12

    b. 21

    c. 22

    d. 32

15. What jersey number did Jeff Bagwell wear for the Astros?

    a. 3

    b. 5

    c. 7

    d. 9

16. What jersey number did Jim Wynn wear for the Colt .45s/Astros?

    a. 8

    b. 18

    c. 24

    d. Both B and C

17. What jersey number does Justin Verlander currently wear for the Astros?

    a. 35

    b. 45

    c. 49

    d. 59

18. What jersey number did Jose Cruz wear as an Astro?

    a. 21
    b. 25
    c. 38
    d. 45

19. What jersey number did Roy Oswalt wear as an Astro?

    a. 22
    b. 33
    c. 44
    d. 55

20. The Astros currently have nine retired uniform numbers.

    a. True
    b. False

QUIZ ANSWERS

1. A – True

2. C – 1975

3. A – True

4. C – 12

5. D – 27

6. D – Both A and B

7. B – False

8. C – L.J. Hoes

9. A – Larry Dierker

10. A – True

11. B – Navy blue, orange, white

12. D – Jim Umbricht

13. A – True

14. C – 22

15. B – 5

16. D – Both B and C

17. A – 35

18. B – 25

19. C – 44

20. A – True

DID YOU KNOW?

1. The Astros have retired nine players and their numbers overall so far. Jim Umbricht (number 32), Don Wilson (number 40), Jose Cruz (number 25), Mike Scott (number 33), Nolan Ryan (number 34), Larry Dierker (number 49), Jim Wynn (number 24), Jeff Bagwell (number 5), and Craig Biggio (number 7).

2. The original Colt .45s home uniforms featured a navy pistol with orange smoke coming out of the barrel to form the letter C.

3. Only two players have ever wore number 99 for the Astros, Mitch Williams in 1994 and Rudy Owens in 2014.

4. John Mayberry is the only Houston Astros player to ever wear the uniform number 00. He wore it back in 1968.

5. From 1980 to 1993, the Astros wore uniforms with rainbow sleeves. They initially began as part of the road uniform but became part of the home uniform as well in 1986.

6. From 1994 to 1999, the Astros changed their uniform colors to midnight navy and gold because they wanted a more serious image.

7. Jackie Robinson's number 42 is retired by the Astros as well as the MLB as a whole. No Astros or MLB player will ever wear number 42 again. The Yankees' Mariano Rivera was the final player to wear it.

8. Gustavo Chacin is the only Houston Astros player to ever wear number 73. He wore it in 2010.

9. Two Astros players wore Bagwell's number 5 before it was retired; Hal King (1967) and Steve Henderson (1988). Six Astros players wore Biggio's number 7 before it was retired; Merritt Ranew (1962), Gus Triandos (1965), John Bateman (1963-68), Johnny Edwards (1969-74), Alan Bannister (1984), and Robbie Wine (1986-87).

10. Orbit, the Astros' mascot wears the uniform number 00.

CHAPTER 3:

FAMOUS QUOTES

QUIZ TIME!

1. Which former Astros player once said: "I think any great performer or athlete has to have a little bit of a gut to be great."?

   a. Craig Biggio
   b. Lance Berkman
   c. Nolan Ryan
   d. Jim Wynn

2. Which current Astros pitcher once said: "On any given night, I can throw a shutout."?

   a. Justin Verlander
   b. Zack Greinke
   c. Roy Oswalt
   d. Nolan Ryan

3. Craig Biggio once said: "Home runs just come from accidents by me. I just try to hit it solid and sometimes they go out. The record is nice to have, but I'm not trying to hit them."

a. True

b. False

4. Which former Astros pitcher once said: "I think anything is possible if you have the mindset and the will and desire to do it and put the time in."?

  a. Mike Scott

  b. Nolan Ryan

  c. Dallas Keuchel

  d. Roger Clemens

5. Who did President Barack Obama once say ate pizza with a fork?

  a. Jose Altuve

  b. Carlos Correa

  c. Hunter Pence

  d. Alex Bregman

6. Which former Astro is quoted as saying: "You've got to have camaraderie or togetherness on a baseball team if you want to win."?

  a. Andy Pettitte

  b. Jeff Bagwell

  c. Moises Alou

  d. Brad Ausmus

7. Which former Astro is quoted as saying: "I never lost confidence in myself, no matter what the years were like or the results."?

  a. Terry Puhl

  b. Billy Wagner

c. J.R. Richard

d. Brad Lidge

8. Former Astro, Nolan Ryan once said: "A life is not important except in the impact it has on other lives."

a. True

b. False

9. Which former Astros manager is quoted as saying: "When I was a kid, I used to play marbles. I know some of you think I've lost mine."?

a. Harry Walker

b. Jimy Williams

c. Terry Collins

d. Art Howe

10. Which Astros manager is quoted as saying: "Everybody knows something, and nobody knows everything."?

a. Bill Virdon

b. Phil Garner

c. Dusty Baker

d. Hal Lanier

11. Which former Astros pitcher is quoted as saying: "My ability to throw a baseball was a God-given gift and I am truly appreciative of that gift."?

a. Roger Clemens

b. Roy Oswalt

c. Nolan Ryan

d. Joe Niekro

12. Which current Astros player is quoted as saying: "If you expect greatness, greatness shouldn't surprise you."?

   a. Jose Altuve
   b. Justin Verlander
   c. George Springer
   d. Josh Reddick

13. Which former Astros player is quoted as saying: "When you're a kid growing up, you say you want to make it to the Major Leagues, and when you do reach that dream, that's what it's all about."?

   a. Joe Morgan
   b. Jose Cruz
   c. Bob Watson
   d. Don Wilson

14. Which former Astro is quoted as saying: "I'm not greedy, I'm not selfish. I just wanted to win a World Series one time."?

   a. Derek Bell
   b. Jeff Bagwell
   c. Lance Berkman
   d. Craig Biggio

15. Which Astros pitcher is quoted as saying: "One of the beautiful things about baseball is that every once in a while, you come into a situation where you want to and where you have to reach down and prove something."?

   a. Nolan Ryan
   b. Joe Niekro

c. Roger Clemens

d. Roy Oswalt

16. Former Astro Craig Biggio once said: "Never allow the fear of striking out keep you from playing the game."

   a. True

   b. False

17. Which Astros player is quoted as saying: "One-run games can go either way, and most of the time, they do." AND "They were chanting my name, but I don't know why. My name is on the back of my uniform. So, it's nice to know they can read."?

   a. Josh Reddick

   b. Zack Greinke

   c. Lance Berkman

   d. Jeff Bagwell

18. Which former Astro once said: "I think you learn to understand although you may be down, you're not out."?

   a. Alan Ashby

   b. Brian McCann

   c. Terry Puhl

   d. Brad Ausmus

19. Which former Astros player once said: "Whenever I get into a tough situation... I think of growing up, and I say, 'This situation won't be the worse one I've ever been in.'"?

   a. Billy Wagner

   b. Brad Lidge

c. Jason Castro
d. Doug Rader

20. Former Astro Nolan Ryan once said: "Maybe I was born to play ball. Maybe I truly was."

   a. True
   b. False

QUIZ ANSWERS

1. B – Lance Berkman

2. C – Roy Oswalt

3. A – True

4. D – Roger Clemens

5. C – Hunter Pence

6. A – Andy Pettitte

7. D – Brad Lidge

8. B – False (Jackie Robinson said it.)

9. B – Jimy Williams

10. C – Dusty Baker

11. C – Nolan Ryan

12. B – Justin Verlander

13. A – Joe Morgan

14. D – Craig Biggio

15. A – Nolan Ryan

16. B – False (Babe Ruth said it.)

17. C – Lance Berkman

18. D – Brad Ausmus

19. A – Billy Wagner

20. B – False (Willie Mays said it.)

DID YOU KNOW?

1. "I still have very close ties to Houston and the Astros because that was my first team." – Joe Morgan

2. "When you're a pitcher for the Houston Astros and a stranger notices you in a mall in Colorado, you know things have really changed." – Brad Lidge

3. "The Houston Astros want to change the name of Enron Field where they play. I guess the Enron name could cause problems for them. Like players could steal a base and then deny it." – Jay Leno

4. "I'd say the average person wouldn't eat a Chipotle burrito and still do his job running full speed like me. That's why they call me special." – Zack Greinke

5. "The only thing I can control is how well I pitch." – Justin Verlander

6. "I love the pressure. I love pitching in situations where it counts." – Roy Oswalt

7. "It helps if the hitter thinks you're a little crazy." – Nolan Ryan

8. "I want to play every game of my career in an Astros uniform." – Lance Berkman

9. "A good base stealer should make the whole infield jumpy. Whether you steal or not, you're changing the rhythm of the game. If the pitcher is concerned about you, he isn't concentrating enough on the batter." – Joe Morgan

10. "I had some pretty special teammates over 20 years, especially my early years where they were the most impressionable. I was around guys like Nolan Ryan, Billy Doran, Buddy Bell, Terry Puhl. Being around these guys taught me how to respect the game and play the game the right way, day in and day out. It was always about the team." – Craig Biggio in his National Baseball Hall of Fame induction speech

CHAPTER 4:

CATCHY NICKNAMES

QUIZ TIME!

1. Which nickname did Roger Clemens go by?

    a. Roger Rabbit

    b. Clemmy

    c. Rocket

    d. Both A and B

2. Jimmy Wynn went by the nickname "The Toy Cannon."

    a. True

    b. False

3. What nickname did Rusty Staub go by?

    a. Orange Rust

    b. Stauby

    c. Le Grande Orange

    d. Rustaub

4. What nickname did Craig Biggio go by?

    a. Big Craig

    b. Bidge

c. Big Man

d. Gio

5. Which is NOT a nickname the Astros as a team have been referred to as?

a. The 'Stros

b. The Astronauts

c. The Space Men

d. The Asterisks

6. Which nickname did Roy Oswalt go by?

a. Ossy

b. Wizard of Os

c. Roy-O

d. Rookie of the Year

7. Brad is a nickname. Brad Ausmus's first name is Bradley.

a. True

b. False

8. Which nickname does Jeff Bagwell go by?

a. Baggy

b. BagPipes

c. BagMan

d. Both A and B

9. What famous nickname does former Astros pitcher Dwight Gooden go by?

a. Good

b. Do Right Dwight

c. So Gooden

d. Doc

10. What nickname did Lance Berkman go by?

    a. Big Puma

    b. Fat Elvis

    c. The Berk-Man

    d. Both A and B

11. What nickname did Jose Cruz go by?

    a. Bullseye

    b. Cheo

    c. Chico

    d. Crazy Cruz

12. Dwight Gooden got the nickname "Doc" because he was a pediatrician during the baseball offseason.

    a. True

    b. False

13. What is J.R. Richard's full name?

    a. Jack Ryan Richard

    b. James Ryan Richard

    c. James Rodney Richard

    d. Jack Rodney Richard

14. What nickname did Enos Cabell go by?

    a. Big E

    b. Cabby

    c. Bell

    d. Eccentric

15. Joe Morgan went by the nicknames "Little Joe" and "The Little General."

    a. True

    b. False

16. Bob Watson went by which nickname?

    a. Bear

    b. Lion

    c. Bull

    d. Scorpion

17. Doug Rader went by the nicknames "Rojo" and "The Red Rooster."

    a. True

    b. False

18. What nickname does Michael Brantley go by?

    a. Dr. Cool

    b. Dr. B

    c. Dr. Fast

    d. Dr. Smooth

19. What nickname did Nolan Ryan go by?

    a. The Life of Ryan

    b. The Ryan Express

    c. Rollin' Nolan

    d. Flyin' Ryan

20. Former Astro Jake Marisnick goes by the nickname Big Vanilla.

a. True
b. False

ANSWERS

1. C – Rocket

2. A – True

3. C – Le Grande Orange

4. B – Bidge

5. C – The Space Men

6. B – Wizard of Os

7. A – True

8. D – Both A and B

9. D – Doc

10. D – Both A and B

11. B – Cheo

12. B – False

13. C – James Rodney Richard

14. A – Big E

15. A – True

16. C – Bull

17. A – True

18. D – Dr. Smooth

19. B – The Ryan Express

20. B – False (Big Fudge)

DID YOU KNOW?

1. Jose Altuve goes by the simple nickname "Tuve."

2. Former Astros catcher Brian McCann goes by the nickname "Heap."

3. Former Astro Evan Gattis goes by the nickname "El Oso Blanco," which means the White Bear.

4. Former Astros pitcher Charlie Morton's nicknames include "Ground Chuck" and "Uncle Charlie."

5. Former Astros pitcher Jose Lima went by the nickname "Lima Time."

6. Former Astros pitcher Billy Wagner went by the nickname "Billy the Kid."

7. Former Astros pitcher Randy Johnson's famous nickname is "The Big Unit."

8. Former Astros pitcher Brad Lidge went by the nickname "Lights Out."

9. Former Astros catcher Ivan Rodriguez's famous nickname is "Pudge."

10. Dwight Gooden led the MLB in strikeouts his first two seasons, which earned him the nickname "Dr. K." Over time, "Dr. K" was eventually shortened to simply "Doc."

CHAPTER 5:

THE RYAN EXPRESS

QUIZ TIME!

1. What is Nolan Ryan's full name?

   a. Nolan Lyle Ryan Jr.

   b. Lyle Nolan Ryan Jr.

   c. Lynn Nolan Ryan Jr.

   d. Nolan Lynn Ryan Jr.

2. During his MLB career, Nolan Ryan played for the Texas Rangers, Houston Astros, New York Mets, and the California Angels.

   a. True

   b. False

3. Where was Nolan Ryan born?

   a. Houston, Texas

   b. Refugio, Texas

   c. Frisco, Texas

   d. Dallas, Texas

4. When was Nolan Ryan born?

    a. January 13, 1947
    b. January 13, 1950
    c. January 31, 1950
    d. January 31, 1947

5. Nolan Ryan threw seven no-hitters in his MLB career.

    a. True
    b. False

6. How many total MLB records does Nolan Ryan currently hold?

    a. 61
    b. 51
    c. 41
    d. 31

7. Where did Nolan Ryan go to high school?

    a. Alvin High School
    b. Clear Creek High School
    c. Westwood High School
    d. Carroll High School

8. When Nolan Ryan was called up to the New York Mets in 1966, he was the second youngest player in the MLB.

    a. True
    b. False

9. Nolan Ryan was previously _____ of the Houston Astros organization.

a. General manager

b. CEO

c. Executive advisor

d. Head scout

10. What is the name of Nolan Ryan's 1992 autobiography?

a. Nolan Ryan's Pitcher's Bible

b. Throwing Heat

c. Miracle Man

d. The Road to Cooperstown

11. Nolan Ryan played in the MLB for how many presidential administrations?

a. 3

b. 5

c. 7

d. 9

12. Nolan Ryan is one of only three players in MLB history to have his uniform number retired by at least three teams.

a. True

b. False

13. What year was Nolan Ryan inducted into the National Baseball Hall of Fame?

a. 1995

b. 1989

c. 1990

d. 1999

14. Nolan Ryan NEVER threw a perfect game and NEVER won a Cy Young Award.

    a. True

    b. False

15. Nolan Ryan is one of only 29 players in MLB history to pitch in ___ different decades.

    a. 3

    b. 4

    c. 5

    d. 6

16. Which team drafted Nolan Ryan?

    a. Texas Rangers

    b. Houston Astros

    c. California Angels

    d. New York Mets

17. Nolan Ryan was named to eight All-Star Games in his career.

    a. True

    b. False

18. How many World Series championships did Nolan Ryan win during his career?

    a. 0

    b. 1

    c. 2

    d. 3

19. Nolan Ryan has a charity whose "mission is to provide resources for youth, education and community development." What is the name of Ryan's charity?

   a. The Ryan Express Foundation

   b. The Ryan Foundation

   c. The Nolan Ryan Foundation

   d. The Nolan Foundation

20. Nolan Ryan used to soak his fingers in pickle juice to avoid and treat blisters.

   a. True

   b. False

QUIZ ANSWERS

1. C – Lynn Nolan Ryan Jr.

2. A – True

3. B – Refugio, Texas

4. D – January 31, 1947

5. A – True

6. B – 51

7. A – Alvin High School

8. A – True

9. C – Executive advisor

10. C – Miracle Man

11. C – 7 (Lyndon B. Johnson, Richard Nixon, Gerald Ford, Jimmy Carter, Ronald Reagan, George H.W. Bush, and Bill Clinton)

12. A – True

13. D – 1999

14. A – True

15. B – 4

16. D – New York Mets

17. A – True

18. B – 1 (1969 with the Mets)

19. C – The Nolan Ryan Foundation

20. A – True

DID YOU KNOW?

1. Nolan Ryan married his high school sweetheart, Ruth.

2. In May of 2000, Nolan Ryan introduced Nolan Ryan Beef to Texas markets. The beef was raised and sold on Ryan's personal ranch.

3. Nolan Ryan's son, Reid, previously served as the Astros' president of business operations.

4. In May of 2014, Nolan Ryan published a cookbook called *The Nolan Ryan Beef and Barbecue Cookbook: Recipes from a Texas Kitchen* full of over 75 recipes.

5. In November of 2016, Nolan Ryan, along with David Ortiz and Barry Larkin, created Dugout Ventures, an equity group that focuses on baseball products and companies.

6. In April of 2000, Nolan Ryan suffered a heart attack and underwent emergency double bypass surgery.

7. Nolan Ryan had an infamous fight/brawl with Robin Ventura in 1993 at Arlington Stadium.

8. Nolan Ryan used to be a newspaper boy. He delivered copies of the *Houston Post* every morning for several years.

9. Nolan Ryan played in the MLB for a whopping 27 years.

10. The New York Mets have never retired Nolan Ryan's number. The Mets are the only team he played for who has not retired his number. The Astros, Rangers, and Angels have.

CHAPTER 6:

STATISTICALLY SPEAKING

QUIZ TIME!

1. Jeff Bagwell holds the Houston Astros franchise record for the most home runs. How many did he hit?

    a. 349

    b. 401

    c. 449

    d. 501

2. Joe Niekro has the most wins in Houston Astros franchise history, with 144 in his Astros career.

    a. True

    b. False

3. Which pitcher holds the Houston Astros record for most shutouts thrown in a single season, with six, in 1973?

    a. Bob Knepper

    b. Dave Roberts

    c. Randy Johnson

    d. Mike Scott

4. Which Houston Astros batter holds the single-season record for strikeouts, with 212, in 2013?

   a. Jose Altuve
   b. Carlos Pena
   c. Jonathan Villar
   d. Chris Carter

5. Which pitcher has the most strikeouts in Houston Astros franchise history with a whopping 1,866?

   a. Roy Oswalt
   b. Nolan Ryan
   c. Don Wilson
   d. J.R. Richard

6. Who has the most stolen bases in Houston Astros franchise history, with 487?

   a. Jeff Bagwell
   b. Jose Altuve
   c. Craig Biggio
   d. Cesar Cedeño

7. Billy Wagner holds the record for most saves in Houston Astros history, with 225.

   a. True
   b. False

8. Who holds the Houston Astros record for being intentionally walked, with 155?

   a. Lance Berkman
   b. Jose Cruz

c. Jeff Bagwell

d. Bob Watson

9. Which player holds the Houston Astros franchise record for home runs in a single season, with 47?

   a. Lance Berkman

   b. Richard Hidalgo

   c. Jeff Bagwell

   d. Alex Bregman

10. Who holds the single-season Houston Astros record for hits, with 225?

   a. Jose Altuve

   b. Craig Biggio

   c. Miguel Tejada

   d. Derek Bell

11. Who holds the single-season Houston Astros record for double plays grounded into, with 32?

   a. Brad Ausmus

   b. Miguel Tejada

   c. Carlos Lee

   d. Doug Rader

12. Jeff Bagwell holds the record for the most sacrifice flies in Houston Astros all-time franchise history, with 102.

   a. True

   b. False

13. Joe Niekro threw the most wild pitches in Houston Astros franchise history with how many?

a. 64

b. 81

c. 128

d. 145

14. Roger Metzger holds the Houston Astros single-season record for most triples. How many did he hit in his record 1973 season?

a. 10

b. 14

c. 15

d. 20

15. Which hitter has the most walks in Houston Astros franchise history, with 1,401?

a. Craig Biggio

b. Jim Wynn

c. Lance Berkman

d. Jeff Bagwell

16. Which Houston Astros hitter holds the all-time franchise record for best overall batting average at .331?

a. Moises Alou

b. Jose Altuve

c. Jeff Bagwell

d. Bob Watson

17. Craig Biggio holds the Houston Astros' record for most runs scored, with 1,844.

a. True

b. False

18. Craig Biggio has the most plate appearances all-time in Houston Astros franchise history with how many?

   a. 10,504
   b. 11,504
   c. 12,504
   d. 13,504

19. Which pitcher holds the Houston Astros franchise record for most saves in a single season, with 44?

   a. Billy Wagner
   b. Jose Valverde
   c. Brad Lidge
   d. Both A and B

20. Nolan Ryan holds the Houston Astros franchise record for most losses, with 117.

   a. True
   b. False

QUIZ ANSWERS

1. C – 449

2. A – True

3. B – Dave Roberts

4. D – Chris Carter

5. B – Nolan Ryan

6. D – Cesar Cedeño

7. A – True

8. C – Jeff Bagwell

9. C – Jeff Bagwell (2000)

10. A – Jose Altuve

11. B – Miguel Tejada (2008)

12. A – True

13. C – 128

14. B – 14

15. D – Jeff Bagwell

16. A – Moises Alou

17. A – True

18. C – 12,504

19. D – Both A and B (Wagner in 2003 and Valverde in 2008)

20. B – False (Larry Dierker holds that record.)

DID YOU KNOW?

1. Larry Dierker threw the most innings in Houston Astros franchise history, with 2,294.1. Coming in second is Joe Niekro who threw 2,270.0 innings.

2. Jeff Bagwell had the best single-season batting average in Houston Astros franchise history at .368 in 1994. Moises Alou comes in the second spot with a batting average of .355 in 2000.

3. Michael Bourn holds the Houston Astros franchise record for stolen base percentage with an 82.48% success rate. Cesar Cedeño holds the Houston Astros franchise record for stolen bases, with 487. Cesar Cedeño also holds the Houston Astros franchise record for the most times caught stealing, with 149.

4. Craig Biggio has the most extra-base hits in Houston Astros franchise history, with 1,014. Second on the list is Jeff Bagwell with 969.

5. Chris Carter holds the Houston Astros franchise record for at-bats per home run at 15.6. Essentially, what this means is that during his time with Houston, Carter hit a home run about every 15-16 at-bats.

6. Billy Wagner holds the Houston Astros franchise record for strikeouts per nine innings pitched at 12.385. Essentially, what this means is that during his time with

Houston, Wagner recorded about 12-13 strikeouts in every nine innings that he pitched.

7. Three pitchers are tied for the single-season Houston Astros record for the most hit by pitches. Jack Billingham hit 16 batters in 1971, Darryl Kile hit 16 batters in 1996, and Charlie Morton hit 16 batters in 2018.

8. Jeff Bagwell holds the Houston Astros franchise record for double plays grounded into, with 221.

9. Mike Hampton holds the Houston Astros single-season record for wins, with 22, in 1999.

10. Turk Farrell holds the Houston Astros single-season record for losses, with 20, in 1962.

CHAPTER 7:

THE TRADE MARKET

QUIZ TIME!

1. On August 31, 2017, the Houston Astros traded Franklin Perez, Daz Cameron, and Jake Rogers to the Detroit Tigers in exchange for whom?

    a. Mike Fiers

    b. Justin Verlander

    c. Doug Fister

    d. Francisco Liriano

2. On August 1, 2016, the Houston Astros traded Josh Fields to the Los Angeles Dodgers in exchange for whom?

    a. Zack Greinke

    b. Bud Norris

    c. Tyler White

    d. Yordan Álvarez

3. The Houston Astros have NEVER made a trade with the Texas Rangers.

    a. True

    b. False

4. On August 30, 1990, the Houston Astros traded Larry Andersen to the Boston Red Sox in exchange for whom?

   a. Jeff Bagwell
   b. Roger Clemens
   c. Carl Everett
   d. Trever Miller

5. The Houston Astros have only made six trades with the Arizona Diamondbacks all time.

   a. True
   b. False

6. What year did the Houston Astros trade Lance Berkman to the New York Yankees?

   a. 2008
   b. 2009
   c. 2010
   d. 2011

7. On July 29, 2010, who did the Houston Astros trade to the Philadelphia Phillies in exchange for Anthony Gose, J.A. Happ, and Jonathan Villar?

   a. Michael Bourn
   b. Roy Oswalt
   c. Brad Lidge
   d. Hunter Pence

8. Which team traded Zack Greinke to the Houston Astros at the trade deadline in 2019?

   a. Kansas City Royals
   b. Los Angeles Dodgers

c. Arizona Diamondbacks

d. Milwaukee Brewers

9. On July 23, 2015, the Houston Astros traded Daniel Mengden and Jacob Nottingham to the Oakland A's in exchange for whom?

a. Josh Reddick

b. Chris Carter

c. Mike Fiers

d. Scott Kazmir

10. The Houston Astros have made only nine trades with the Colorado Rockies all time.

a. True

b. False

11. On January 19, 2015, the Houston Astros traded Dexter Fowler to the Chicago Cubs in exchange for Dan Straily and whom?

a. Anthony Bass

b. Scott Feldman

c. Luis Valbuena

d. Cameron Maybin

12. On August 18, 2009, the Houston Astros traded Ivan Rodriguez back to the Texas Rangers.

a. True

b. False

13. How many trades have the Houston Astros made with the Oakland A's?

a. 5

b. 10

c. 15

d. 20

14. The Houston Astros NEVER traded Craig Biggio or Jeff Bagwell.

    a. True

    b. False

15. On February 4, 2013, the Houston Astros traded Jed Lowrie and Fernando Rodriguez Jr. to which team in exchange for Max Stassi, Brad Peacock, and Chris Carter?

    a. Los Angeles Angels of Anaheim

    b. Oakland A's

    c. Los Angeles Dodgers

    d. New York Yankees

16. On December 18, 1981, who did the Houston Astros trade to the Cincinnati Reds in exchange for Ray Knight?

    a. Cesar Cedeño

    b. Buddy Bell

    c. C.J. Nitkowski

    d. Joe Morgan

17. How many trades have the Houston Astros made with the Los Angeles Dodgers all time?

    a. 3

    b. 12

    c. 23

    d. 33

18. On December 6, 1973, who did the Houston Astros trade to the Los Angeles Dodgers in exchange for Claude Osteen and David Culpepper?

    a. Enos Cabell
    b. Willie Crawford
    c. Bob Stinson
    d. Jim Wynn

19. On July 30, 2015, the Houston Astros traded Josh Hader, Adrian Houser, Brett Phillips, and Domingo Santana to which team in exchange for Mike Fiers and Carlos Gomez?

    a. Texas Rangers
    b. Milwaukee Brewers
    c. New York Mets
    d. Minnesota Twins

20. On November 23, 1976, the Houston Astros traded Larry Dierker and Jerry DaVanon to the St. Louis Cardinals in exchange for Bob Detherage and Joe Ferguson.

    a. True
    b. False

QUIZ ANSWERS

1. B – Justin Verlander

2. D – Yordan Álvarez

3. B – False (10 trades as of the end of the 2019 season)

4. A – Jeff Bagwell

5. A – True

6. C – 2010

7. B – Roy Oswalt

8. C – Arizona Diamondbacks

9. D – Scott Kazmir

10. A – True

11. C – Luis Valbuena

12. A – True

13. C – 15

14. A – True (They both played their entire careers with Houston.)

15. B – Oakland A's

16. A – Cesar Cedeño

17. B – 12

18. D – Jim Wynn

19. B – Milwaukee Brewers

20. A – True

DID YOU KNOW?

1. On November 29, 1971, the Houston Astros traded Joe Morgan, Ed Armbrister, Jack Billingham, Cesar Geronimo, and Denis Menke to the Cincinnati Reds in exchange for Tommy Helms, Lee May, and Jimmy Stewart.

2. On December 10, 1982, the Houston Astros traded Danny Heep to the New York Mets in exchange for Mike Scott.

3. On September 15, 1985, the Houston Astros traded Joe Niekro to the New York Yankees for players to be named later (Neder Horta and Dody Rather) and Jim Deshaies.

4. On December 28, 1994, the Houston Astros traded a player to be named later, Ken Caminiti, Andujar Cedeno, Steve Finley, Roberto Petagine, and Brian Williams to the San Diego Padres in exchange for Derek Bell, Doug Brocail, Pedro Martinez, Ricky Gutierrez, Phil Plantier, and Craig Shipley. Bell was traded by the Astros to the New York Mets in 1999 with Mike Hampton in exchange for Octavio Dotel, Roger Cedeño, and Kyle Kessel.

5. On January 10, 1991, the Houston Astros traded Glenn Davis to the Baltimore Orioles in exchange for Curt Schilling, Steve Finley, and Pete Harnisch. On April 2, 1992, the Houston Astros traded Curt Schilling to the Philadelphia Phillies for Jason Grimsley.

6. On December 11, 1975, the Houston Astros traded Doug

Rader to the San Diego Padres in exchange for Larry Hardy and Joe McIntosh.

7. On November 11, 1997, the Houston Astros traded a player to be named later (Mark Johnson), Manuel Barrios, and Oscar Henriquez to the Florida Marlins in exchange for Moises Alou.

8. On August 30, 1990, the Houston Astros traded Bill Doran to the Cincinnati Reds for players to be named later (Terry McGriff, Keith Kaiser, and Butch Henry).

9. On June 13, 1979, the Houston Astros traded Bob Watson to the Boston Red Sox in exchange for a player to be named later (Bobby Sprowl), Pete Ladd, and cash.

10. On July 29, 2011, the Houston Astros traded Hunter Pence and cash to the Philadelphia Phillies in exchange for a player to be named later (Domingo Santana), Jarred Cosart, Jon Singleton, and Josh Zeid.

CHAPTER 8:

DRAFT DAY

QUIZ TIME!

1. Which MLB team drafted Astros legend Jeff Bagwell in the 4th round of the 1989 MLB Draft?

   a. Oakland Athletics
   b. Los Angeles Dodgers
   c. Boston Red Sox
   d. New York Yankees

2. With the 22nd overall pick in the 1st round of the 1987 MLB Draft, who did the Houston Astros select?

   a. Bill Doran
   b. Craig Biggio
   c. Kevin Bass
   d. Terry Puhl

3. With the 16th overall pick in the 1st round of the 1997 MLB Draft, who did the Houston Astros select?

   a. Derek Bell
   b. Tim Bogar

c. Mike Hampton

d. Lance Berkman

4. With the 19th overall pick in the 1st round of the 1983 MLB Draft, who selected Roger Clemens?

   a. New York Mets

   b. Boston Red Sox

   c. New York Yankees

   d. Toronto Blue Jays

5. With the 2nd overall pick in the 1st round of the 2015 MLB Draft, who did the Houston Astros select?

   a. George Springer

   b. Carlos Correa

   c. Jose Altuve

   d. Alex Bregman

6. With the 2nd overall pick in the 1st round of the 1969 MLB Draft, who did the Houston Astros pick?

   a. Joe Morgan

   b. J.R. Richard

   c. Doug Rader

   d. Jim Wynn

7. Carlos Correa was drafted 1st overall by the Houston Astros in the 2012 MLB Draft.

   a. True

   b. False

8. Nolan Ryan was drafted in the 12th round of the 1965 MLB Draft by which team?

a. New York Mets

b. California Angels

c. Texas Rangers

d. None of the above

9. With the 10th overall pick in the 1st round of the 2008 MLB Draft, the Houston Astros selected catcher Jason Castro out of which school?

a. San Diego State University

b. University of California at Berkeley

c. San Francisco State University

d. Stanford University

10. The Houston Astros drafted right-hander Roy Oswalt in the 23rd round of the 1996 MLB Draft.

a. True

b. False

11. With the 11th overall pick in the 1st round of which MLB Draft, did the Houston Astros select right fielder George Springer?

a. 2010

b. 2011

c. 2012

d. 2013

12. With the 1st overall pick in the 1st round of the 1998 MLB Draft, the Houston Astros selected pitcher Brad Lidge.

a. True

b. False

13. In the 2nd round of the 1976 MLB Draft, which team selected pitcher Mike Scott out of Pepperdine University?

    a. Kansas City Royals

    b. San Francisco Giants

    c. New York Mets

    d. Houston Astros

14. In which round of the 2009 MLB Draft, did the Houston Astros select lefty Dallas Keuchel?

    a. 1st

    b. 2nd

    c. 5th

    d. 7th

15. Former Astros catcher Brad Ausmus was drafted by which team in the 48th round of the 1987 MLB Draft?

    a. New York Yankees

    b. San Diego Padres

    c. Detroit Tigers

    d. Los Angeles Dodgers

16. Former Astros pitcher Andy Pettitte was drafted by the New York Yankees in which round of the 1990 MLB Draft?

    a. 2nd

    b. 10th

    c. 22nd

    d. 30th

17. The Houston Astros selected second baseman Bill Doran in which round of the 1979 MLB Draft?

a. 3rd

b. 4th

c. 5th

d. 6th

18. Justin Verlander was drafted by the Detroit Tigers with which pick in the 1st round of the 2004 MLB Draft?

    a. 1st

    b. 2nd

    c. 3rd

    d. 8th

19. Zack Greinke was drafted in the 1st round, 6th overall in the 2002 MLB Draft by which team?

    a. Arizona Diamondbacks

    b. Los Angeles Dodgers

    c. Kansas City Royals

    d. Milwaukee Brewers

20. The Astros' first ever 1st round draft pick was shortstop Alex Barrett in 1965. He was chosen 4th overall.

    a. True

    b. False

QUIZ ANSWERS

1. C – Boston Red Sox

2. B – Craig Biggio

3. D – Lance Berkman

4. B – Boston Red Sox

5. D – Alex Bregman

6. B – J.R. Richard

7. A – True

8. A – New York Mets

9. D – Stanford University

10. A – True

11. B – 2011

12. B – False

13. C – New York Mets

14. D – 7th

15. A – New York Yankees

16. C – 22nd

17. D – 6th

18. B – 2nd

19. C – Kansas City Royals

20. A – True

DID YOU KNOW?

1. The Houston Astros drafted right fielder Hunter Pence in the 2nd round of the 2004 MLB Draft out of the University of Texas at Arlington.

2. The Cleveland Indians drafted former Astros catcher Alan Ashby in the 3rd round of the 1969 MLB Draft out of high school.

3. The Milwaukee Brewers drafted former Astros right fielder Kevin Bass in the 2nd round of the 1977 MLB Draft out of high school.

4. Michael Bourn was drafted by the Houston Astros in the 19th round of the 2000 Draft out of high school but did not sign. He was then drafted by the Philadelphia Phillies in the 4th round of the 2003 MLB Draft out of the University of Houston. He ended up playing four years of his career with the Astros.

5. Carlos Beltran was drafted out of high school in Puerto Rico by the Kansas City Royals in the 2nd round of the 1995 MLB Draft.

6. The Chicago Cubs drafted former Astros right-hander Joe Niekro in the 3rd round of the 1966 MLB Draft out of West Liberty University.

7. The Pittsburgh Pirates drafted former Astros outfielder Moises Alou with the 2nd overall pick in the 1986 MLB Draft out of Canada College.

8. The Houston Astros drafted Delino DeShields Jr. in the 1st round of the 2010 MLB Draft (8th overall). His father played in the MLB for 13 seasons, but never played for the Astros.

9. The Houston Astros drafted Lance McCullers Jr. in the 1st round of the 2012 MLB Draft (41st overall). His father played in the MLB for seven seasons, but never played for the Astros.

10. The Seattle Mariners drafted former Astros left-hander Mike Hampton in the 6th round of the 1990 MLB Draft out of high school.

CHAPTER 9:

ODDS & ENDS

QUIZ TIME!

1. Gerrit Cole is the brother-in-law of which San Francisco Giants player?

    a. Buster Posey

    b. Brandon Crawford

    c. Brandon Belt

    d. Evan Longoria

2. Moises Alou's father, Felipe, was his manager during his time with the Montreal Expos and San Francisco Giants.

    a. True

    b. False

3. Art Howe is portrayed by which actor in the movie *Moneyball*?

    a. Brad Pitt

    b. Jonah Hill

    c. Chris Pratt

    d. Philip Seymour Hoffman

4. Roy Oswalt won a gold medal in men's baseball representing the U.S.A. in what year?

   a. 1992

   b. 1996

   c. 2000

   d. 2004

5. Justin Verlander is married to which model?

   a. Kate Upton

   b. Gigi Hadid

   c. Gisele Bündchen

   d. Chrissy Teigen

6. Former Astro Jeff Kent appeared on which TV reality show?

   a. Big Brother

   b. Survivor

   c. The Amazing Race

   d. American Ninja Warrior

7. Jose Altuve is the shortest active player in Major League Baseball.

   a. True

   b. False

8. Zack Greinke is a minority owner of a franchise for which fast food chain?

   a. In-N-Out

   b. Dunkin Donuts

   c. Chipotle

   d. Ben & Jerry's

9. Footage of Jim Wynn rounding third base is featured in which space movie?

    a. Interstellar
    b. Space Cowboys
    c. The Martian
    d. Apollo 13

10. Terry Puhl was manager of which nation's baseball team?

    a. Italy
    b. Dominican Republic
    c. Mexico
    d. Canada

11. Which former Astros player became a pitching coach for a high school team alongside another former Astro, Lance Berkman?

    a. Roy Oswalt
    b. Andy Pettitte
    c. Nolan Ryan
    d. Mike Hampton

12. Brad Lidge currently hosts a radio show on SiriusXM's MLB Network Radio.

    a. True
    b. False

13. Former Astro Bill Doran named his son after which of his Astros teammates?

    a. Terry Puhl
    b. Craig Biggio

c. Kevin Bass

d. Nolan Ryan

14. Carlos Lee currently owns and operates cattle ranches in Houston.

    a. True

    b. False

15. Lance McCullers Jr.'s dad, Lance McCullers, played in the MLB from 1985 to 1992. He played for the New York Yankees, Detroit Tigers, Texas Rangers, and which other team?

    a. Houston Astros

    b. San Diego Padres

    c. Los Angeles Dodgers

    d. Oakland A's

16. Kevin Bass is cousins with former NFL player and coach James Lofton.

    a. True

    b. False

17. Which Astros player proposed to his girlfriend on live TV after winning the 2017 World Series?

    a. Jose Altuve

    b. Alex Bregman

    c. Carlos Correa

    d. Josh Reddick

18. Who was George Springer's favorite baseball player while growing up?

a. Craig Biggio
b. Mike Piazza
c. Vladimir Guerrero
d. Torii Hunter

19. Justin Verlander's parents wrote a book about the story of his development as a person and a player. What is the title of that 2012 book?

a. Rocks Across the Pond: Lessons Learned, Stories Told
b. Verlander: The Story of How Our Son Made it to the Big Leagues
c. Justin: From Little Boy to Big Leaguer
d. Sliding into Home: The Justin Verlander Story

20. Shane Reynolds's brother is actor Ryan Reynolds.

a. True
b. False

QUIZ ANSWERS

1. B – Brandon Crawford

2. A – True

3. D – Philip Seymour Hoffman

4. C – 2000

5. A – Kate Upton

6. B – Survivor

7. A – True

8. C – Chipotle

9. D – Apollo 13

10. D – Canada

11. B – Andy Pettitte

12. A – True

13. D – Nolan Ryan (He named his son Ryan.)

14. A – True

15. B – San Diego Padres

16. A – True

17. C – Carlos Correa

18. D – Torii Hunter

19. A – Rocks Across the Pond: Lessons Learned, Stories Told

20. B – False

DID YOU KNOW?

1. Hunter Pence's wife, Lexi, has a YouTube channel that often features content with her and Hunter. The channel is called "Let's Get Lexi."

2. Craig Biggio bats and throws right-handed, but writes left-handed.

3. In March 2020, George Springer donated $100,000 to Minute Maid Park employees during the COVID-19 pandemic.

4. George Springer suffers from a stutter. He is a spokesman for the Stuttering Association for the Young and does charity work for the cause as well.

5. Josh Reddick is an avid wrestling fan. He even wrote an article about his love for wrestling in *The Player's Tribune*.

6. Max Stassi's great-uncle, Myril Hoag, played in three World Series. He played from 1931 to 1945 for the New York Yankees, St. Louis Browns, Chicago White Sox, and Cleveland Indians. Max's brother Brock also played in the MLB.

7. Brad Ausmus was inducted into the National Jewish Sports Hall of Fame in 2004.

8. Dusty Baker was a member of the United States Marine Corps Reserve from 1968 to 1974.

9. Moises Alou did not wear batting gloves. Instead, he urinated on his hands to "toughen them up."

10. J.A. Happ is a first cousin of former Wisconsin Badgers basketball player Ethan Happ.

CHAPTER 10:

OUTFIELDERS

QUIZ TIME!

1. Hunter Pence played five seasons with the Houston Astros. Which of the teams below has he NOT played for during his 14-season career?

   a. San Francisco Giants
   b. Philadelphia Phillies
   c. Texas Rangers
   d. Los Angeles Angels of Anaheim

2. Former Astros outfielder Lance Berkman did NOT win a World Series championship over the course of his 15-season MLB career.

   a. True
   b. False

3. How many Silver Slugger Awards did former Astros outfielder Moises Alou win over the course of his 17-year MLB career?

   a. 0
   b. 2

c. 5

d. 10

4. Cesar Cedeño was NEVER named to an All-Star Game in his 17-year MLB career.

   a. True

   b. False

5. Jim Wynn played 11 seasons with the Houston Astros. Which of the teams below did he NOT play for during his 15-season career?

   a. Milwaukee Brewers

   b. Los Angeles Dodgers

   c. San Diego Padres

   d. Atlanta Braves

6. Former Astros outfielder Jose Cruz played for three teams in his 19-season MLB career; the Astros, New York Yankees, and which other team?

   a. Los Angeles Dodgers

   b. St. Louis Cardinals

   c. Boston Red Sox

   d. Chicago Cubs

7. Enos Cabell played eight seasons with the Houston Astros.

   a. True

   b. False

8. How many All-Star Games was outfielder Terry Puhl named to over the course of his 15-season career?

a. 1

b. 2

c. 3

d. 4

9. How many Gold Glove Awards did former Astros outfielder Michael Bourn win over the course of his 11-season MLB career?

a. 0

b. 1

c. 2

d. 3

10. How many Silver Slugger Awards did former Astros outfielder Carlos Lee win over the course of his 14-season career?

a. 1

b. 2

c. 3

d. 4

11. Richard Hidalgo played for the Houston Astros for eight seasons. He played for two other teams over the course of his MLB career: the New York Mets and which other franchise?

a. Philadelphia Phillies

b. San Francisco Giants

c. Toronto Blue Jays

d. Texas Rangers

12. Kevin Bass collected 990 hits over his 10 seasons with the Houston Astros.

    a. True
    b. False

13. How many home runs did Astros outfielder Josh Reddick hit during the 2018 season?

    a. 13
    b. 14
    c. 17
    d. 20

14. How many World Series championships did former Astros outfielder Steve Finley win during his career?

    a. 0
    b. 1
    c. 2
    d. 3

15. How many All-Star Games was centerfielder Carlos Beltran named to over the course of his 20-season MLB career?

    a. 4
    b. 6
    c. 9
    d. 13

16. Which Astros outfielder was named the 2017 World Series MVP?

    a. Josh Reddick
    b. George Springer

c. Nori Aoki

d. Jake Marisnick

17. How many seasons did outfielder Luis Gonzalez spend with the Houston Astros?

    a. 5

    b. 6

    c. 7

    d. 8

18. What place did Gerald Young come in for 1987 NL Rookie of the Year voting?

    a. 2nd

    b. 3rd

    c. 4th

    d. 5th

19. How many Gold Glove Awards did Cesar Cedeño win during his MLB career?

    a. 3

    b. 4

    c. 5

    d. 6

20. Moises Alou NEVER won a World Series championship in his MLB career.

    a. True

    b. False

QUIZ ANSWERS

1. D – Los Angeles Angels of Anaheim

2. B – False (He won in 2011 with the St. Louis Cardinals.)

3. B – 2

4. B – False (He is a four-time All-Star.)

5. C – San Diego Padres

6. B – St. Louis Cardinals

7. A – True

8. A – 1

9. C – 2

10. B – 2

11. D – Texas Rangers

12. A – True

13. C – 17

14. B – 1 (2001 with the Arizona Diamondbacks)

15. C – 9

16. B – George Springer

17. C – 7

18. D – 5th

19. C – 5

20. B – False (He won in 1997 with the Florida Marlins.)

DID YOU KNOW?

1. Lance Berkman played 1,592 games total for the Houston Astros, the most of any team he played for over the course of his 15-year MLB career. He also played for the St. Louis Cardinals, Texas Rangers, and New York Yankees.

2. Cesar Cedeño played 1,512 games total for the Houston Astros, the most of any team he played for over the course of his 17-year MLB career. He also played for the Cincinnati Reds, St. Louis Cardinals, and Los Angeles Dodgers.

3. Jim Wynn played 1,426 games total for the Houston Astros, the most of any team he played for over the course of his 15-year MLB career. He also played for the Los Angeles Dodgers, New York Yankees, Atlanta Braves, and Milwaukee Brewers.

4. Jose Cruz played 1,870 games total for the Houston Astros, the most of any team he played for over the course of his 19-year MLB career. He also played for the St. Louis Cardinals and the New York Yankees.

5. Hunter Pence played 680 games for the Houston Astros in his five seasons spent with the team. He has also played for the San Francisco Giants, Philadelphia Phillies, and Texas Rangers.

6. Enos Cabell played 1,067 games for the Houston Astros, the most of any team he played for over the course of his

15-year MLB career. He also played for the Baltimore Orioles, Los Angeles Dodgers, Detroit Tigers, and San Francisco Giants.

7. Moises Alou played 421 games total in the three seasons he spent with the Houston Astros. Over the course of his 17-year MLB career, he also played for the Montreal Expos, Chicago Cubs, New York Mets, San Francisco Giants, Pittsburgh Pirates, and Florida Marlins.

8. Terry Puhl played 1,516 games for the Houston Astros, the most of any team he played for over the course of his 15-year MLB career. He played 14 of those seasons with Houston and spent one season with the Kansas City Royals.

9. Michael Bourn played 541 games total in the four seasons he spent with the Houston Astros, the most of any team he played for over the course of his 11-year MLB career. He also played for the Atlanta Braves, Cleveland Indians, Philadelphia Phillies, Arizona Diamondbacks, and Baltimore Orioles.

10. Carlos Lee played 815 games for the Houston Astros in the six seasons spent with the team. He also played for the Chicago White Sox, Milwaukee Brewers, Texas Rangers, and Miami Marlins.

CHAPTER 11:

INFIELDERS

QUIZ TIME!

1. Which former Astros manager was an infielder during his playing days?

    a. Bill Virdon

    b. Art Howe

    c. Larry Dierker

    d. Dave Clark

2. Joe Morgan hit 268 home runs over the course of his 22-year MLB career.

    a. True

    b. False

3. What place did Lance Berkman come in for NL Rookie of the Year voting in 2000?

    a. 2nd

    b. 4th

    c. 6th

    d. 8th

4. How many home runs did Jose Altuve hit in his 2019 season?

   a. 17
   b. 24
   c. 31
   d. 40

5. Over the course of his 12-year MLB career, Bill Doran played for the Astros, Milwaukee Brewers, and which other team?

   a. Cincinnati Reds
   b. Los Angeles Dodgers
   c. New York Yankees
   d. Minnesota Twins

6. What year was Carlos Correa named American League Rookie of the Year?

   a. 2014
   b. 2015
   c. 2016
   d. 2017

7. Bob Watson was named to two All-Star Games over the course of his 19-year MLB career.

   a. True
   b. False

8. What year did Alex Bregman win a Silver Slugger Award?

   a. 2016
   b. 2017

c. 2018

d. 2019

9. What year was Alex Bregman named All-Star Game MVP?

 a. 2016

 b. 2017

 c. 2018

 d. 2019

10. How many Gold Glove Awards did Doug Rader win over the course of his 11-year MLB career?

 a. 0

 b. 2

 c. 3

 d. 5

11. How many stolen bases did Craig Biggio accumulate during his 20-year MLB career?

 a. 404

 b. 414

 c. 424

 d. 434

12. Miguel Tejada is a two-time Silver Slugger Award winner.

 a. True

 b. False

13. How many times was Ty Wigginton named to the All-Star Game in his 12-year MLB career?

 a. 0

 b. 1

c. 2

d. 3

14. How many home runs did Yuli Gurriel hit in his 2019 season?

    a. 17

    b. 24

    c. 31

    d. 40

15. What year was Joe Morgan named to the National Baseball Hall of Fame?

    a. 1989

    b. 1990

    c. 1991

    d. 1993

16. Jeff Kent was named to the All-Star Game five times in his 17-year MLB career.

    a. True

    b. False

17. How many All-Star Games was Jed Lowrie named to over the course of his 12-year MLB career?

    a. 0

    b. 1

    c. 2

    d. 3

18. How many home runs did Chris Carter hit in his 2014 season?

a. 11

b. 25

c. 37

d. 41

19. How many Silver Slugger Awards did Carlos Lee win over the course of his 14-year MLB career?

a. 0

b. 2

c. 3

d. 4

20. Jose Altuve was named American League MVP in 2017.

a. True

b. False

ANSWERS

1. B – Art Howe

2. A – True

3. C – 6th

4. C – 31

5. A – Cincinnati Reds

6. B – 2015

7. A – True

8. D – 2019

9. C – 2018

10. D – 5

11. B – 414

12. A – True

13. B – 1

14. C – 31

15. B – 1990

16. A – True

17. B – 1

18. C – 37

19. B – 2

20. A – True

DID YOU KNOW?

1. Second baseman Joe Morgan played for the Houston Astros for 10 seasons. He also played for the Cincinnati Reds, San Francisco Giants, Philadelphia Phillies, and Oakland A's. He is a member of the National Baseball Hall of Fame, a two-time MVP, 10-time All-Star, two-time World Series champion, five-time Gold Glove Award winner, Silver Slugger Award winner, and All-Star Game MVP. He played 1,032 games total with the Astros.

2. First baseman Lance Berkman played for the Houston Astros for 12 seasons. He also played for the St. Louis Cardinals, Texas Rangers, and New York Yankees. He is a six-time All-Star and World Series champion. He played 1,592 games total with the Astros.

3. Second baseman Jose Altuve has played for the Houston Astros for 10 seasons. At this point in his career, he is an AL MVP, six-time All-Star, World Series champion, Gold Glove Award winner, five-time Silver Slugger Award winner, three-time batting title winner, and ALCS MVP.

4. Shortstop Carlos Correa has played for the Houston Astros for six seasons. At this point in his career, he is a Rookie of the Year Award winner, All-Star, and World Series champion.

5. Third baseman Alex Bregman has played for the Houston Astros for five seasons. At this point in his career, he is a

two-time All-Star, World Series champion, Silver Slugger Award winner, and All-Star Game MVP.

6. First baseman Carlos Lee played for the Houston Astros for six seasons. He also played for the Chicago White Sox, Milwaukee Brewers, Texas Rangers, and Miami Marlins. He is a three-time All-Star and two-time Silver Slugger Award winner. He played 815 games total with the Astros.

7. Infielder Doug Rader played for the Houston Astros for nine seasons. He also played for the San Diego Padres and Toronto Blue Jays. He is a five-time Gold Glove Award winner (He won them all consecutively.). He played 1,178 games total with the Astros.

8. First baseman Bob Watson played for the Houston Astros for 14 seasons. He also played for the Atlanta Braves, New York Yankees, and Boston Red Sox. He is a two-time All-Star. He played 1,381 games total with the Astros.

9. Craig Biggio played his entire 20-year MLB career with the Houston Astros. He is a member of the National Baseball Hall of Fame, a seven-time All-Star, four-time Gold Glove Award and five-time Silver Slugger Award winner. He played a whopping 2,850 games total with the Astros.

10. First baseman Yuli Gurriel has played for the Houston Astros for five seasons. He is a 2017 World Series Champion. He came in 4th place in 2017 AL Rookie of the Year voting.

CHAPTER 12:

PITCHERS & CATCHERS

QUIZ TIME!

1. Former Astros catcher Brad Ausmus has been manager for the Detroit Tigers and which other team?

   a. Houston Astros

   b. Los Angeles Angels of Anaheim

   c. Oakland A's

   d. Kansas City Royals

2. Former Astros pitcher Roy Oswalt NEVER won a World Series championship in his 13-year MLB career.

   a. True

   b. False

3. How many All-Star Games was former Astros pitcher Roger Clemens named to over the course of his 24-year MLB career?

   a. 6

   b. 9

   c. 11

   d. 15

4. How many World Series championships did Nolan Ryan win in his 27-year MLB career?

    a. 0
    b. 1
    c. 3
    d. 4

5. How many Gold Glove Awards has former Astros pitcher Dallas Keuchel won?

    a. 1
    b. 2
    c. 3
    d. 4

6. How many Cy Young Awards has Astros pitcher Justin Verlander won so far in his career?

    a. 1
    b. 2
    c. 3
    d. 4

7. Former Astros pitcher Randy Johnson was named to 10 All-Star Games in his 22-year MLB career.

    a. True
    b. False

8. How many Silver Slugger Awards did former Astros catcher Brian McCann win in his 15-year MLB career?

    a. 0
    b. 3

c. 6

d. 9

9. Former Astros catcher Jason Castro was named to the All-Star Game in which season?

   a. 2013

   b. 2014

   c. 2015

   d. 2016

10. How many Silver Slugger Awards did former Astros pitcher Mike Hampton win in his 16-year MLB career?

    a. 0

    b. 2

    c. 4

    d. 5

11. Over the course of his 22-year MLB career, pitcher Joe Niekro played for the Houston Astros, New York Yankees, Detroit Tigers, Minnesota Twins, Atlanta Braves, San Diego Padres, and which other franchise?

    a. Los Angeles Dodgers

    b. Chicago Cubs

    c. Chicago White Sox

    d. Oakland A's

12. Catcher Alan Ashby was drafted by the Houston Astros in the 3rd round of the 1969 MLB Draft.

    a. True

    b. False

13. How many All-Star Games was former Astros pitcher Larry Dierker named to in his 14-year MLB career?

    a. 0
    b. 1
    c. 2
    d. 5

14. How many career saves does former Astros pitcher Billy Wagner have?

    a. 222
    b. 322
    c. 422
    d. 522

15. Former Astros pitcher Dave Smith played for two teams in his 13-season MLB career. He played for the Astros and which other team?

    a. San Diego Padres
    b. Chicago Cubs
    c. Cincinnati Reds
    d. Boston Red Sox

16. Former Astros pitcher Brad Lidge has 225 career saves.

    a. True
    b. False

17. Which Astros pitcher won the NL ERA title in 1979?

    a. Ken Forsch
    b. Rick Williams
    c. Joe Niekro
    d. J.R. Richard

18. How many times did Nolan Ryan win the NL ERA title in his 27-year MLB career?

    a. 0
    b. 1
    c. 2
    d. 4

19. How many Gold Glove Awards has current Astros pitcher Zack Greinke won so far in his career?

    a. 2
    b. 4
    c. 6
    d. 8

20. Pitcher Don Wilson played his entire nine-year MLB career with the Houston Astros.

    a. True
    b. False

QUIZ ANSWERS

1. B – Los Angeles Angels of Anaheim

2. A – True

3. C – 11

4. B – 1 (1969 with the Mets)

5. D – 4

6. B – 2

7. A – True

8. C – 6

9. A – 2013

10. D – 5

11. B – Chicago Cubs

12. B – False (Cleveland Indians)

13. C – 2

14. C – 422

15. B – Chicago Cubs

16. A – True

17. D – J.R. Richard

18. C – 2

19. C – 6

20. A – True

DID YOU KNOW?

1. Pitcher Roger Clemens played for the Houston Astros for three seasons. Over the course of his 24-year MLB career, he also played for the Boston Red Sox, New York Yankees, and Toronto Blue Jays. He is a seven-time Cy Young Award winner, an 11-time All-Star, a seven-time ERA title winner, MVP, two-time Triple Crown winner, two-time World Series champion, and All-Star MVP. His record with the Astros was 38-18.

2. Catcher Brad Ausmus played for the Houston Astros for 10 seasons. Over the course of his 18-year MLB career, he also played for the San Diego Padres, Detroit Tigers, and Los Angeles Dodgers. He was an All-Star and three-time Gold Glove Award winner. He has managed the Detroit Tigers and the Los Angeles Angels of Anaheim so far in his coaching career.

3. Pitcher Roy Oswalt played for the Houston Astros for 10 seasons. Over the course of his 13-year MLB career, he also played for the Philadelphia Phillies, Colorado Rockies, and Texas Rangers. He was a three-time All-Star, ERA title winner, and NLCS MVP. His record with the Astros was 143-82.

4. Pitcher Nolan Ryan played for the Houston Astros for nine seasons, the most of any team he ever played for. Over the course of his 27-year MLB career, he also played for the

Texas Rangers, New York Mets, and California Angels. He was named to the National Baseball Hall of Fame in 1999 with 98.8% of the vote, is an eight-time All-Star, two-time ERA title winner, and a 1969 World Series champion with the Mets. He never won a Cy Young Award. His record with the Astros was 106-94.

5. Pitcher Larry Dierker played for the Houston Astros for 13 seasons. He also played for the St. Louis Cardinals for one season. He was a two-time All-Star and was named the 1998 NL Manager of the Year when he was manager of the Astros. His pitching record with the Astros was 137-117.

6. Craig Biggio began his career with the Astros as a catcher. He played his entire 20 seasons in the MLB with the Astros. He was named to the National Baseball Hall of Fame in 2015. He is a seven-time All-Star, four-time Gold Glove Award winner, and five-time Silver Slugger Award winner. His son, Cavan, currently plays in the big leagues for the Toronto Blue Jays.

7. Current Astros pitcher Justin Verlander has been with the team since 2017. The only other MLB team he has played for in his career is the Detroit Tigers. He was with the Tigers for 13 years. Verlander is an MVP, two-time Cy Young Award winner, Rookie of the Year Award winner, Triple Crown winner, eight-time All-Star, ERA title winner, ALCS MVP, and World Series champion.

8. Current Astros pitcher Zack Greinke has been with the team since 2019. He has also played for the Kansas City

Royals, Arizona Diamondbacks, Los Angeles Dodgers, Milwaukee Brewers, and Los Angeles Angels of Anaheim. Greinke is a Cy Young Award winner, six-time All-Star, six-time Gold Glove Award winner, two-time Silver Slugger Award winner, and two-time ERA title winner.

9. Catcher Alan Ashby played for the Houston Astros for 11 seasons. Over the course of his 17-year MLB career, he also played for the Cleveland Indians and Toronto Blue Jays.

10. There have been 13 no-hitters in Houston Astros franchise history. The list of Astros no-hitters in order are: Don Nottebart, Ken Johnson, Don Wilson (2), Larry Dierker, Ken Forsch, Nolan Ryan, Mike Scott, Darryl Kile; a combined effort that featured Roy Oswalt, Peter Munro, Kirk Saarloos, Brad Lidge, Octavio Dotel, and Billy Wagner; Mike Fiers; a combined effort featuring Aaron Sanchez, Will Harris, Joe Biagini, and Chris Devenski; and Justin Verlander. However, no Astros pitcher has ever completed a perfect game in the team's history.

CHAPTER 13:

WORLD SERIES

QUIZ TIME!

1. How many World Series have the Houston Astros won in franchise history?

    a. 0

    b. 1

    c. 2

    d. 3

2. How many NL pennants have the Houston Astros won?

    a. 0

    b. 1

    c. 2

    d. 3

3. How many AL pennants have the Houston Astros won?

    a. 0

    b. 1

    c. 2

    d. 3

4. Which team did the Houston Astros face in the 2005 World Series?

    a. Kansas City Royals
    b. Tampa Bay Rays
    c. Boston Red Sox
    d. Chicago White Sox

5. Which team did the Houston Astros face in the 2017 World Series?

    a. Los Angeles Dodgers
    b. New York Mets
    c. San Francisco Giants
    d. Washington Nationals

6. Which team did the Houston Astros face in the 2019 World Series?

    a. Los Angeles Dodgers
    b. New York Mets
    c. San Francisco Giants
    d. Washington Nationals

7. George Springer was named the 2017 World Series MVP.

    a. True
    b. False

8. Who was the Houston Astros' manager during their 2005 World Series run?

    a. Jimy Williams
    b. Phil Garner
    c. Cecil Cooper
    d. Art Howe

9. Who was the Houston Astros' manager during their 2017 and 2019 World Series runs?

   a. Bo Porter

   b. Brad Mills

   c. A.J. Hinch

   d. Dusty Baker

10. How many games did the 2005 World Series go?

   a. 4

   b. 5

   c. 6

   d. 7

11. How many games did the 2017 World Series go?

   a. 4

   b. 5

   c. 6

   d. 7

12. The 2019 World Series went 7 games.

   a. True

   b. False

13. Which Astro did NOT hit a home run in the 2005 World Series?

   a. Morgan Ensberg

   b. Craig Biggio

   c. Mike Lamb

   d. Jason Lane

14. Which Astro did NOT hit a home run in the 2017 World Series?

   a. Jose Altuve
   b. Alex Bregman
   c. Josh Reddick
   d. Carlos Correa

15. Which Astro did NOT hit a home run in the 2019 World Series?

   a. Jose Altuve
   b. Carlos Correa
   c. George Springer
   d. Alex Bregman

16. The Houston Astros have never earned a wild card berth.

   a. True
   b. False

17. Which team did the Houston Astros face in the 2005 NLCS to advance to the World Series?

   a. Los Angeles Dodgers
   b. St. Louis Cardinals
   c. Cincinnati Reds
   d. Florida Marlins

18. Which team did the Houston Astros face in the 2017 ALCS to advance to the World Series?

   a. Detroit Tigers
   b. Tampa Bay Rays
   c. Oakland A's
   d. New York Yankees

19. Which team did the Houston Astros face in the 2019 ALCS to advance to the World Series?

    a. Detroit Tigers
    b. Tampa Bay Rays
    c. Oakland A's
    d. New York Yankees

20. When the Astros won the 2017 World Series, the city of Houston was in the midst of Hurricane _____.

    a. Ike
    b. Harvey
    c. Allison
    d. Alicia

QUIZ ANSWERS

1. B – 1

2. B – 1 (2005)

3. C – 2 (2017 & 2019)

4. D – Chicago White Sox

5. A – Los Angeles Dodgers

6. D – Washington Nationals

7. A – True

8. B – Phil Garner

9. C – A.J. Hinch

10. A – 4

11. D – 7

12. A – True

13. B – Craig Biggio

14. C – Josh Reddick

15. A – Jose Altuve

16. B – False (2004, 2005, 2015)

17. B – St. Louis Cardinals

18. D – New York Yankees

19. D – New York Yankees

20. 20. B – Harvey

DID YOU KNOW?

1. It was discovered that the Houston Astros committed sign stealing during the 2017 World Series. This has tainted their title and caused an uproar among MLB players and fans. Both A.J. Hinch and GM Jeff Luhnow were suspended by the MLB and were fired by the Astros. The team was fined $5 million and lost several draft picks. MLB Commissioner Rob Manfred decided not to punish players or revoke their title.

2. The 2005 World Series is one of only two World Series in the modern era with no possibility for a rematch because the Astros moved to the American League in 2013. The Chicago White Sox are members of the American League as well.

3. The 2017 World Series was the first in which home field advantage was determined by which team had the best regular season record.

4. Jose Altuve, Alex Bregman, Carlos Correa, Marwin Gonzalez, Yuli Gurriel, Brian McCann, Josh Reddick, and George Springer all played in all seven games of the 2017 World Series.

5. Jose Altuve, Yordan Álvarez, Michael Brantley, Alex Bregman, Carlos Correa, Yuli Gurriel, and George Springer all played in all seven games of the 2019 World Series.

6. The 2005 World Series took place from October 22 to October 26. The 2017 World Series took place from October 24 to November 1. The 2019 World Series took place from October 22 to October 30.

7. Game 1 of the 2005 World Series took place at U.S. Cellular Field in Chicago. Luis Aparicio threw out the first pitch, and Josh Groban sang the national anthem. Game 4 of the 2005 World Series took place at Minute Maid Park in Houston. Juan Marichal threw out the first pitch, and Jon Secada sang the national anthem.

8. Game 1 of the 2017 World Series took place at Dodger Stadium in Los Angeles. Rachel Robinson (Jackie Robinson's wife), Sharon Robinson (Jackie Robinson's daughter), and David Robinson (Jackie Robinson's son) threw out the first pitches, and Keith Williams Jr. sang the national anthem. Game 7 of the 2017 World Series took place at Dodger Stadium in Los Angeles. Sandy Koufax and Don Newcombe threw the ceremonial first pitches to Steve Garvey and Rick Monday, and the LAPD quartet sang the national anthem.

9. Game 1 of the 2019 World Series took place at Minute Maid Park in Houston. Brian McCann threw out the first pitch, and Nicole Scherzinger sang the national anthem. Game 7 of the 2019 World Series took place at Minute Maid Park in Houston. Jeff Bagwell and Craig Biggio threw out the first pitches, and Cody Johnson sang the national anthem.

10. The 43rd President of the United States George W. Bush threw out the first pitch before Game 5 of the 2017 World Series at Minute Maid Park to Justin Verlander.

CHAPTER 14:

HEATED RIVALRIES

QUIZ TIME!

1. Which team does NOT play in the American League West with the Astros?

   a. Oakland A's
   b. Los Angeles Dodgers
   c. Seattle Mariners
   d. Texas Rangers

2. The Astros are a founding member of the AL West division.

   a. True
   b. False

3. Which team was NOT formerly a member of the AL West?

   a. Minnesota Twins
   b. Kansas City Royals
   c. Toronto Blue Jays
   d. Chicago White Sox

4. What division did the Astros play in from 1969 to 1993?

    a. American League Central

    b. National League East

    c. National League West

    d. National League Central

5. What division did the Astros play in from 1994 to 2012?

    a. American League Central

    b. National League East

    c. National League West

    d. National League Central

6. The Houston Astros have one World Series championship. How many do the Texas Rangers have?

    a. 0

    b. 1

    c. 2

    d. 3

7. The Astros have the most AL West championships of any team in the division.

    a. True

    b. False

8. Which player has NOT played for both the Astros and the Texas Rangers?

    a. Lance Berkman

    b. Roy Oswalt

    c. Jason Castro

    d. Nolan Ryan

9. Which player has NOT played for both the Astros and the Oakland A's?

    a. Josh Reddick

    b. Mike Fiers

    c. Miguel Tejada

    d. Justin Verlander

10. Which player has NOT played for both the Astros and the Los Angeles Angels of Anaheim?

    a. Lance Berkman

    b. Zack Greinke

    c. Scott Kazmir

    d. Nolan Ryan

11. Which player has NOT played for both the Astros and the Seattle Mariners?

    a. Mike Hampton

    b. Joe Morgan

    c. J.A. Happ

    d. Randy Johnson

12. The Houston Astros and Texas Rangers have NEVER faced each other in the World Series.

    a. True

    b. False

13. Who is the only player in MLB history to be named the DHL Hometown Hero for two teams (both the Rangers and Astros)?

    a. Roy Oswalt

    b. Lance Berkman

c. Nolan Ryan

d. Ivan Rodriguez

14. When the Houston Astros play the Texas Rangers, what is the series called?

    a. Texas Series

    b. Gold Boot Series

    c. Cowboy Series

    d. Lone Star Series

15. How many rainouts have there been in the history of the Lone Star Series?

    a. 0

    b. 1

    c. 3

    d. 6

16. The Houston Astros and Texas Rangers have NEVER met in the MLB postseason.

    a. True

    b. False

17. Before the Houston Astros moved to the American League West, a trophy was given to the winner of the interleague Lone Star Series. What was the name of that trophy?

    a. The Lone Star

    b. The Silver Boot

    c. The Gold Cowboy Hat

    d. The Bronze Horse

18. When was the first meeting of the Lone Star Series?

    a. June 8, 1999

    b. September 6, 2001

    c. June 8, 2001

    d. September 6, 1999

19. What size shoe was the Silver Boot trophy from Houston Astros and Texas Rangers interleague play?

    a. 12

    b. 13

    c. 14

    d. 15

20. The Houston Astros defeated the Rangers on March 31, 2013, their first game as a member of the American League West division.

    a. True

    b. False

QUIZ ANSWERS

1. B – Los Angeles Dodgers

2. B – False (joined in 2013)

3. C – Toronto Blue Jays

4. C – National League West

5. D – National League Central

6. A – 0

7. B – False (Oakland A's have 17.)

8. C – Jason Castro

9. D – Justin Verlander

10. A – Lance Berkman

11. B – Joe Morgan

12. A – True

13. C – Nolan Ryan

14. D – Lone Star Series

15. B – 1

16. A – True

17. B – The Silver Boot

18. C – June 8, 2001

19. D – 15

20. A – True

DID YOU KNOW?

1. The Oakland A's have the most World Series wins in the American League West, with nine. The Seattle Mariners and Texas Rangers both have never won the World Series. The Los Angeles Angels of Anaheim and the Houston Astros have one World Series win each. The Oakland A's have the most American League West division championships, with 17 total. The Los Angeles Angels of Anaheim have won nine AL West division championships, then comes the Rangers with seven, and finally the Astros with three (although they have only been in the AL West since 2013).

2. Although pitcher Nolan Ryan played for both the Houston Astros and the Texas Rangers, he chose to have his National Baseball Hall of Fame plaque adorned with a Rangers hat. In retirement, he has worked for both the Astros' and Rangers' front offices.

3. During a radio interview in 2017, Rangers manager Jeff Bannister was quoted as saying, "All I know is they get to put Houston on their chest. We get to put Texas on ours." Astros pitcher Lance McCullers Jr. slammed him back on Twitter saying, "It's because nobody knows what Arlington is."

4. The Houston Astros joined the American League West in 2013. The Astros and Rangers had previously only played

each other in interleague play since 2001. This was actually to help ease the Texas Rangers' schedule. Before the Astros joined, the Rangers were the only team in the American League West who were not on Pacific time. The Astros joining allowed more time flexibility and gave the Rangers a closer team to play against. Although, this did heighten the Lone Star Rivalry even more.

5. The Houston Astros won the World Series in 2017, which was the first World Championship for a team from the state of Texas.

6. In 2015, the Rangers won the American League West division, and the Astros won a wild card berth. The Astros playoff slogan/campaign that season was "Come and Take It!". The Rangers taunted the Astros by claiming "We Came and Took it!".

7. Although the Astros have been in Texas for 10 more years than the Rangers, the Rangers franchise is one year older than the Astros. The Texas Rangers franchise began as the Washington Senators in 1961, and the Houston Astros franchise began as the Houston Colt .45s in 1962.

8. Carlos Beltran, Lance Berkman, Travis Blackley, Bruce Chen, Robinson Chirinos, Scott Feldman, Armando Galarraga, Carlos Gomez, Richard Hidalgo, Carlos Lee, Kenny Lofton, Phil Nevin, C.J. Nitkowski, Roy Oswalt, Carlos Pena, Hunter Pence, Dave Roberts, Ivan Rodriguez, Nolan Ryan, Rusty Staub, Jerome Williams, and Mitch Williams have all played for both the Astros and the Texas Rangers.

9. Fernando Abad, Travis Blackley, Chris Carter, Tyler Clippard, Octavio Dotel, Mike Fiers, Robbie Grossman, Stan Javier, Scott Kazmir, Matt Keough, Don Larsen, Jed Lowrie, Joe Morgan, Pat Neshek, Carlos Pena, Josh Reddick, Kirk Saarloos, Dan Straily, and Miguel Tejada have all played for both the Astros and the Oakland A's.

10. Bobby Abreu, Pat Borders, Jason Castro, Steve Finley, Dustin Garneau, Zack Greinke, LaTroy Hawkins, Stan Javier, Scott Kazmir, Cameron Maybin, Phil Nevin, Bud Norris, Nolan Ryan, Max Stassi, Luis Valbuena, Jerome Williams, and Mitch Williams have all played for both the Astros and the Los Angeles Angels of Anaheim.

CHAPTER 15:

THE AWARDS SECTION

QUIZ TIME!

1. Which Houston Astros pitcher won a National League Cy Young Award in 2004?

    a. Roy Oswalt

    b. Roger Clemens

    c. Andy Pettitte

    d. Brad Lidge

2. No Houston Astros pitcher has ever won an American League Cy Young Award.

    a. True

    b. False

3. Which Houston Astros player won a Silver Slugger Award in 1998?

    a. Craig Biggio

    b. Moises Alou

    c. Jeff Bagwell

    d. Both A and B

4. Which Houston Astros player most recently won the Rookie of the Year Award?

   a. Jeff Bagwell
   b. Craig Biggio
   c. Carlos Correa
   d. Yordan Álvarez

5. Who is the only player in Houston Astros history to win the Roberto Clemente Award?

   a. Jose Altuve
   b. Craig Biggio
   c. Jeff Bagwell
   d. Carlos Lee

6. Who is the only player in Houston Astros history to win the All-Star Game MVP Award?

   a. Jose Altuve
   b. Lance Berkman
   c. Alex Bregman
   d. Nolan Ryan

7. No Houston Astros manager has ever won a Manager of the Year Award.

   a. True
   b. False

8. Which Astros player was named the DHL Hometown Hero? (Voted by MLB fans as the most outstanding player in franchise history.)

   a. Nolan Ryan
   b. Jeff Bagwell

c. Craig Biggio

d. Jimmy Wynn

9. Who was the first Houston Astros player to win a National League Gold Glove Award?

a. Doug Rader

b. Cesar Cedeño

c. Roger Metzger

d. Jeff Bagwell

10. How many Silver Slugger Awards did Craig Biggio win during his time with the Houston Astros?

a. 2

b. 4

c. 5

d. 7

11. Which Houston Astros player was given the Babe Ruth Award (best postseason performance) in 2017?

a. Jose Altuve

b. Justin Verlander

c. Josh Reddick

d. Both A and B

12. Jose Altuve was named the 2017 American League MVP.

a. True

b. False

13. Who was named the 1999 National League Rolaids Relief Man of the Year?

a. Trever Miller

b. Billy Wagner

c. Jay Powell

d. Brian Williams

14. Which Astros player was named the 2005 NLCS MVP?

a. Roy Oswalt

b. Lance Berkman

c. Brad Ausmus

d. Jose Vizcaino

15. What year were the Houston Astros named the Baseball America Organization of the Year?

a. 1998

b. 2001

c. 2013

d. 2017

16. No Houston Astros player has ever won the Home Run Derby.

a. True

b. False

17. Which Houston Astros player won the 1995 ESPY Award for Best Breakthrough Athlete?

a. Craig Biggio

b. Derrick May

c. Derek Bell

d. Jeff Bagwell

18. How many Gold Glove Awards did Brad Ausmus win during his time with the Houston Astros?

    a. 1

    b. 2

    c. 3

    d. 4

19. How many NL Gold Glove Awards did Craig Biggio win during his time with the Houston Astros?

    a. 2

    b. 4

    c. 5

    d. 7

20. Jeff Bagwell was named the 1994 National League MVP.

    a. True

    b. False

QUIZ ANSWERS

1. B – Roger Clemens

2. B – False (Dallas Keuchel in 2015, Justin Verlander in 2019)

3. D – Both A and B

4. D – Yordan Álvarez (2019)

5. B – Craig Biggio (2007)

6. C – Alex Bregman (2018)

7. B – False (Hal Lanier in 1986, Larry Dierker in 1998)

8. A – Nolan Ryan

9. A – Doug Rader (1970)

10. C – 5 (1989, 1994, 1995, 1997, 1998)

11. D – Both A and B

12. A – True

13. B – Billy Wagner

14. A – Roy Oswalt

15. B – 2001

16. A – True

17. D – Jeff Bagwell

18. C – 3 (2001, 2002, 2006)

19. B – 4 (1994, 1995, 1996, 1997)

20. A – True

DID YOU KNOW?

1. The Houston Astros have four different pitchers who have been named Cy Young Award winners in franchise history: Mike Scott (1986, NL), Roger Clemens (2004, NL), Dallas Keuchel (2015, AL), and Justin Verlander (2019, AL).

2. The Houston Astros had nine different players win Silver Slugger Awards when they were a part of the National League: Dickie Thon, Jose Cruz, Glenn Davis, Craig Biggio, Jeff Bagwell, Moises Alou, Mike Hampton, Morgan Ensberg, and Carlos Lee. Four different players have won Silver Slugger Awards since the Astros became a member of the American League: Jose Altuve, George Springer, Alex Bregman, and Zack Greinke.

3. The Houston Astros have three different players who have been named Rookie of the Year in franchise history: Jeff Bagwell (1991, NL), Carlos Correa (2015, AL), and Yordan Álvarez (2019, AL).

4. Two Houston Astros broadcasters have been named winners of the Ford C. Frick Award in franchise history: Milo Hamilton (1992) and Gene Elston (2006).

5. Only two Houston Astros players have ever been named league MVP in franchise history: Jeff Bagwell (1994, NL) and Jose Altuve (2017, AL).

6. The Astros' Gold Glove Award winners in the NL were

Doug Rader, Cesar Cedeño, Roger Metzger, Jeff Bagwell, Craig Biggio, Brad Ausmus, and Michael Bourn. Houston's AL Gold Glove Award winners were Dallas Keuchel, Jose Altuve, and Zack Greinke.

7. George Springer was named the 2017 World Series MVP.

8. Two Houston Astros players have been named NLCS MVP in franchise history: Mike Scott (1986) and Roy Oswalt (2005). Two Houston Astros players have been named ALCS MVP in franchise history: Justin Verlander (2017) and Jose Altuve (2019).

9. No Houston Astros manager has been named the American League Manager of the Year.

10. The first Houston Astros players to win a Silver Slugger Award were Jose Cruz and Dickie Thon in 1983.

CHAPTER 16:

SPACE CITY

QUIZ TIME!

1. What is the name of the NASA facility in Houston?

    a. Goddard Space Center

    b. Glenn Space Center

    c. Johnson Space Center

    d. Armstrong Space Center

2. "Houston" was the first word heard from the moon.

    a. True

    b. False

3. The average Houston resident eats out an average of how many times per week?

    a. 3.2

    b. 4.8

    c. 5.1

    d. 6.9

4. Which music superstar was born in Houston?

    a. Lady Gaga

    b. Ariana Grande

    c. Miley Cyrus

    d. Beyonce

5. Houston is the __ most populous city in the United States.

    a. 2nd

    b. 3rd

    c. 4th

    d. 8th

6. Houston hosts the world's largest _____ show.

    a. Livestock

    b. Art

    c. Drag

    d. Both A and B

7. Houston is home to the world's largest medical center.

    a. True

    b. False

8. Which singer had a hit song called "Houston"?

    a. Frank Sinatra

    b. Bruce Springsteen

    c. Michael Jackson

    d. Dean Martin

9. What is the name of Houston's NFL team?

    a. Houston Rangers

    b. Houston Texans

c. Houston Cowboys

d. Houston Giants

10. What is the name of Houston's NBA team?

   a. Houston Nets

   b. Houston Pistons

   c. Houston Warriors

   d. Houston Rockets

11. What is the name of the Texans' stadium?

   a. Nissan Stadium

   b. Arrowhead Stadium

   c. NRG Stadium

   d. State Farm Stadium

12. Houston does not have an NHL team.

   a. True

   b. False

13. What is the name of the Rockets' arena?

   a. Target Center

   b. Chase Center

   c. American Airlines Center

   d. Toyota Center

14. Which food was invented in Houston?

   a. Chocolate chip cookies

   b. Fajitas

   c. French fries

   d. Burritos

15. Houston is named after _____.

    a. Whitney Houston

    b. Margaret Lea Houston

    c. Sam Houston

    d. Walter Scott Houston

16. Houston has a National Museum of Funeral History.

    a. True

    b. False

17. The Houston Zoo is the ____ most visited zoo in the United States.

    a. 2nd

    b. 4th

    c. 5th

    d. 7th

18. Which airport is located in Houston?

    a. George Bush Intercontinental Airport

    b. William P. Hobby Airport

    c. Jack Brooks Regional Airport

    d. Both A and B

19. Which movie was filmed in Houston?

    a. Independence Day

    b. Selena

    c. Transformers: Dark of the Moon

    d. All of the above

20. Houston hosted the 1974, 2004, and 2017 NFL Super Bowls.

   a. True
   b. False

QUIZ ANSWERS

1. C – Johnson Space Center

2. B – False

3. D – 6.9

4. D – Beyonce

5. C – 4th

6. A – Livestock

7. A – True (Houston Texas Medical Center)

8. D – Dean Martin

9. B – Houston Texans

10. D – Houston Rockets

11. C – NRG Stadium

12. A – True

13. D – Toyota Center

14. B – Fajitas

15. C – Sam Houston

16. A – True

17. A – 2nd

18. D – Both A and B

19. D – All of the above

20. A – True

DID YOU KNOW?

1. One Direction's "Drag Me Down" music video was filmed at the Johnson Space Center in Houston.

2. Houston's MLS team is the Houston Dynamo. Houston also had a WNBA team, the Houston Comets.

3. Houston is home to Texas's largest shopping mall, the Houston Galleria. It contains 345 stores and is the 9th largest mall in the United States.

4. The Houston Downtown Aquarium is home to over 200 species of aquatic animals, a restaurant, a bar, and a banquet facility.

5. The Houston region is home to Rice University, the University of Houston, and Texas A&M University.

6. More heart surgeries are performed at Texas Medical Center than anywhere else in the world.

7. Houston is home to the world's tallest pentagonal building, the JPMorgan Chase Tower downtown. It is 1,002 feet tall.

8. Houston has the second largest theater district in the United States, after New York City.

9. Houston is known as the world capital of space exploration, the world capital of air conditioning, the world capital of the international energy industry, and the world capital of petroleum exploration.

10. The phone on the International Space Station has a Houston area code (281).

CHAPTER 17:

KILLER B'S

QUIZ TIME!

1. Where was Jeff Bagwell born?

    a. San Diego, California

    b. Boston, Massachusetts

    c. Providence, Rhode Island

    d. Las Vegas, Nevada

2. Jeff Bagwell spent his entire 15-season MLB career with the Houston Astros. Craig Biggio spent his entire 20-season MLB career with the Houston Astros.

    a. True

    b. False

3. What year was Craig Biggio named to the National Baseball Hall of Fame?

    a. 2013

    b. 2014

    c. 2015

    d. 2016

4. What year was Jeff Bagwell named to the National Baseball Hall of Fame?

    a. 2014
    b. 2015
    c. 2016
    d. 2017

5. Where was Craig Biggio born?

    a. Smithtown, New York
    b. Boston, Massachusetts
    c. Fort Worth, Texas
    d. Tampa, Florida

6. How many Silver Slugger Awards did Jeff Bagwell win over the course of his career?

    a. 1
    b. 3
    c. 4
    d. 7

7. Craig Biggio did not win a Silver Slugger Award during his career.

    a. True
    b. False

8. How many All-Star Games was Jeff Bagwell named to in his MLB career?

    a. 1
    b. 2
    c. 4
    d. 7

9. How many All-Star Games was Craig Biggio named to in his MLB career?

    a. 1
    b. 2
    c. 4
    d. 7

10. How many Gold Glove Awards did Jeff Bagwell win over the course of his career?

    a. 1
    b. 2
    c. 4
    d. 7

11. How many Gold Glove Awards did Craig Biggio win over the course of his career?

    a. 1
    b. 2
    c. 4
    d. 7

12. Both Craig Biggio and Jeff Bagwell have their uniform numbers retired by the Houston Astros.

    a. True
    b. False

13. What year was Jeff Bagwell named the NL MVP?

    a. 1993
    b. 1994
    c. 1995
    d. 1996

14. Craig Biggio was drafted by the Houston Astros. Jeff Bagwell was drafted by which team?

    a. Houston Astros
    b. Texas Rangers
    c. Chicago Cubs
    d. Boston Red Sox

15. What year was Jeff Bagwell named the National League Rookie of the Year?

    a. 1989
    b. 1990
    c. 1991
    d. 1992

16. Craig Biggio won a Roberto Clemente Award in 2007.

    a. True
    b. False

17. How many total home runs did Jeff Bagwell hit in his MLB career?

    a. 409
    b. 449
    c. 509
    d. 549

18. How many total home runs did Craig Biggio hit in his MLB career?

    a. 291
    b. 391
    c. 491
    d. 591

19. Craig Biggio's son, Cavan Biggio, currently plays in the MLB for which franchise?

    a. Houston Astros

    b. Boston Red Sox

    c. New York Yankees

    d. Toronto Blue Jays

20. Craig Biggio was the first member of the National Baseball Hall of Fame to be depicted as an Astro on his plaque.

    a. True

    b. False

QUIZ ANSWERS

1. B – Boston, Massachusetts

2. A – True

3. C – 2015

4. D – 2017

5. A – Smithtown, New York

6. B – 3

7. B – False (He won 5.)

8. C – 4

9. D – 7

10. A – 1

11. C – 4

12. A – True

13. B – 1994

14. D – Boston Red Sox

15. C – 1991

16. A – True

17. B – 449

18. A – 291

19. D – Toronto Blue Jays

20. A – True

DID YOU KNOW?

1. Jeff Bagwell was the National League RBI Leader in 1994. Craig Biggio was the National League Stolen Base Leader in 1994.

2. Craig Biggio stole 414 bases in his career. Jeff Bagwell stole 202.

3. Craig Biggio throws and bats right-handed but writes with his left hand.

4. Craig Biggio spent several seasons as the head coach of St. Thomas High School's varsity baseball team in Houston.

5. Jeff Bagwell's 79.6 wins above replacement (WAR) ranks sixth-most all-time among first basemen, trailing only Lou Gehrig, Albert Pujols, Jimmie Foxx, Cap Anson, and Roger Connor.

6. Neither Bagwell nor Biggio ever won a World Series championship.

7. Jeff Bagwell was elected to the Texas Sports Hall of Fame in 2005.

8. Since 2008, Craig Biggio has served as the Astros' special assistant to the general manager.

9. "Another East Coast kid who just loved to play the game. We played 15 years together and changed the culture in Houston by making it a baseball town. We both got to live our dreams together by playing in the big leagues side by

side. Thanks for being here today. It really means a lot." – Craig Biggio on Jeff Bagwell in his National Baseball Hall of Fame speech

10. "My last teammate I want to talk about obviously is Craig Biggio. Thank you, kid, for that wonderful intro. That was great. Craig Biggio I've watched his entire career. When I first came up, he was a catcher. Played second base, center field, back to second base. Craig could do anything that he wanted to. You'll never meet a player who put more effort and time into his craft than Craig. You know, as I sit here today and we go in the Hall of Fame, Craig and I ... pretty much in Houston, we've been known to be together. It was Bagwell and Biggio, Biggio and Bagwell, however you want to say it, but now we'll always be here in the Hall of Fame together. I know his whole entire family, Patty and the kids, and just our relationship that has grown over so many years. And I can't thank you enough for just giving me inspiration to how to play every single day, post and go out there, give everything you can. And Craig and I just wanted to win, and we wanted to win one way, and that was the right way, and I hope that's what we did, and I really thank Craig for that." – Jeff Bagwell in his National Baseball Hall of Fame Speech

CHAPTER 18:

BIG PUMA

QUIZ TIME!

1. Where was Lance Berkman born?

   a. Charleston, South Carolina

   b. Waco, Texas

   c. Louisville, Kentucky

   d. Jacksonville, Florida

2. Lance Berkman returned to his college alma mater in 2014 to finish his degree.

   a. True

   b. False

3. Lance Berkman played for four MLB teams over the course of his 15-season MLB career; the Astros, the St. Louis Cardinals, the Texas Rangers, and which other team?

   a. Chicago Cubs

   b. Minnesota Twins

   c. New York Yankees

   d. Oakland Athletics

4. What year was Lance Berkman born?

    a. 1972

    b. 1975

    c. 1976

    d. 1981

5. How many All-Star Games was Lance Berkman named to over the course of his 15-season MLB career?

    a. 3

    b. 6

    c. 8

    d. 10

6. What year was Lance Berkman named the National League Comeback Player of the Year?

    a. 2011

    b. 2012

    c. 2013

    d. 2014

7. Lance Berkman NEVER won a World Series championship.

    a. True

    b. False

8. How many Gold Glove Awards did Lance Berkman win over the course of his 15-season MLB career?

    a. 0

    b. 3

    c. 6

    d. 9

9. What year was Lance Berkman named the National League RBI Leader?

    a. 2000

    b. 2001

    c. 2002

    d. 2003

10. How many total home runs did Lance Berkman hit over the course of his MLB career?

    a. 326

    b. 366

    c. 426

    d. 466

11. How many RBIs did Lance Berkman collect over the course of his MLB career?

    a. 834

    b. 934

    c. 1,134

    d. 1,234

12. Lance Berkman signed a one-day contract with Houston at the end of his career to officially retire as an Astro.

    a. True

    b. False

13. How many stolen bases did Lance Berkman collect over the course of his MLB career?

    a. 76

    b. 86

c. 96

d. 106

14. What is Lance Berkman's career batting average?

    a. .273

    b. .283

    c. .293

    d. .303

15. How many hits did Lance Berkman collect over the course of his MLB career?

    a. 1,905

    b. 2,005

    c. 2,105

    d. 2,205

16. Lance Berkman holds the Minute Maid Park record for most home runs at the stadium.

    a. True

    b. False

17. Lance Berkman is tied with whom for the National League record for most home runs in a single season as a switch hitter, with 45?

    a. Pete Rose

    b. Mickey Mantle

    c. Roberto Alomar

    d. Chipper Jones

18. How many seasons did Lance Berkman hit better than .300?

a. 2

b. 4

c. 5

d. 7

19. In his MLB debut, Berkman played against the Detroit Tigers. His final game in the MLB was against which team?

a. Kansas City Royals

b. Tampa Bay Rays

c. Colorado Rockies

d. New York Mets

20. Lance Berkman was drafted by the Houston Astros.

a. True

b. False

QUIZ ANSWERS

1. B – Waco, Texas

2. A – True

3. C – New York Yankees

4. C – 1976

5. B – 6

6. A – 2011

7. B – False (2011 with the Cardinals)

8. A – 0

9. C – 2002

10. B – 366

11. D – 1,234

12. A – True

13. B – 86

14. C – .293

15. A – 1,905

16. A – True

17. D – Chipper Jones

18. C – 5

19. B – Tampa Bay Rays

20. A – True

DID YOU KNOW?

1. Forbes recognized Berkman on their list of 30 Most Generous Celebrities in 2012. Berkman's Bunch was an outreach program for underprivileged kids to meet Berkman before each Saturday home game for autographs and gifts. In 2013, he purchased a fire truck and donated it to the city of West, Texas.

2. As of 2015, Lance Berkman is serving as the head baseball coach at Second Baptist School in Houston, Texas. His former Astros teammate Andy Pettitte served as an assistant coach and helped lead Second Baptist to a Tapps State Title in 2016.

3. Lance Berkman holds the National League record for most RBIs (136) in a season as a switch hitter.

4. Lance Berkman held the record for most career home runs at Great American Ballpark in Cincinnati for an opposing player until it was broken recently by Ryan Braun.

5. Lance Berkman was eligible for the National Baseball Hall of Fame in 2019. He received five votes (1.4%), which is less than the 5% threshold and became ineligible for further consideration.

6. Lance Berkman was inducted into the Texas Sports Hall of Fame in 2009.

7. Lance Berkman was given the Darryl Kile Good Guy Award in 2006.

8. Berkman was also one of the Astros' "Killer B's" in the mid-2000s, along with Jeff Bagwell, Craig Biggio, and Derek Bell.

9. When Lance Berkman was a member of the Astros, a fan club called the Little Pumas was created. Fans dressed up in puma costumes and were often featured on Astros broadcasts.

10. Lance Berkman attended Rice University in Houston.

CONCLUSION

Learn anything new? Now you truly are the ultimate Astros fan! Not only did you learn about the Astros of the modern era, but you also expanded your knowledge back to the early days of the franchise.

You learned about the Astros' origins and their history. You learned about the history of their uniforms and jersey numbers. You identified some famous quotes and read some of the craziest nicknames of all time. You learned more about powerhouse hitters Lance Berkman, Craig Biggio, and Jeff Bagwell. You also learned about pitching legend Nolan Ryan. You were amazed by Astros stats and recalled some of the most infamous Astros trades and draft picks of all time. You broke down your knowledge by outfielders, infielders, pitchers, and catchers. You looked back on the Astros' championship, playoff feats, and the awards that came before, after, and during them. You also learned about the Astros' fiercest rivalries, both within their division and outside it.

Every team in the MLB has a storied history, but the Astros have one of the most memorable of all. They have won one World Series with the backing of their devoted fans. Being the ultimate Astros fan takes knowledge and a whole lot of patience, which you tested with this book. Whether you knew every answer or were stumped by several questions, you learned some of the most baffling history that the game of baseball has to offer.

The deep history of the Astros represents what we all love about the game of baseball: the heart, the determination, the tough times, and the unexpected moments. These players inspire us and encourage us to do our best because even if you get knocked down, there is always another game and another day.

With players like Jose Altuve, Carlos Correa, and Alex Bregman, the future for the Astros continues to look bright. They have a lot to prove after their sign-stealing scandal, but there is no doubt that this franchise will continue to be one of the most competitive teams in Major League Baseball year after year.

It's a new decade, which means there is a clean slate, ready to continue writing the history of the Houston Astros. The ultimate Astros fan cannot wait to see what's to come for their beloved 'Stros.

Made in the USA
Coppell, TX
14 October 2023

22863773R00089